MEI structured mathematics

Decision and Discrete Mathematics

CHRIS COMPTON
GEOFF RIGBY

MEI Structured Mathematics is supported by industry:
BNFL, Casio, GEC, Intercity, JCB, Lucas, The National Grid Company,
Texas Instruments, Thorn EMI

Hodder & Stoughton

MEMBER OF THE HODDER HEADLINE GROUP

British Library Cataloguing in Publication Data

Rigby, Geoff
  Decision and Discrete Mathematics. –
  (MEI Structured Mathematics Series)
  I. Title II. Compton, Chris III. Series
  510

ISBN 0 340 57171 3

First published 1992
Impression number   10 9 8 7 6 5
Year   2002 2001 2000 1999 1998 1997

Typeset by Keyset Composition, Colchester, Essex.
Printed in Great Britain for Hodder & Stoughton Educational,
a division of Hodder Headline Plc, 338 Euston Road,
London NW1 3BH by Scotprint Ltd, Musselburgh, Scotland.

MEI Structured Mathematics

Mathematics is not only a beautiful and exciting subject in its own right but also one that underpins many other branches of learning. It is consequently fundamental to the success of a modern economy.

MEI Structured Mathematics is designed to increase substantially the number of people taking the subject post-GCSE, by making it accessible, interesting and relevant to a wide range of students.

It is a credit accumulation scheme based on 45 hour components which may be taken individually or aggregated to give:

3 Components	AS Mathematics
6 Components	A Level Mathematics
9 Components	A Level Mathematics + AS Further Mathematics
12 Components	A Level Mathematics + A Level Further Mathematics

Components may alternatively be combined to give other A or AS certifications (in Statistics, for example) or they may be used to obtain credit towards other types of qualification.

The course is examined by the Oxford and Cambridge Schools Examination Board, with examinations held in January and June each year.

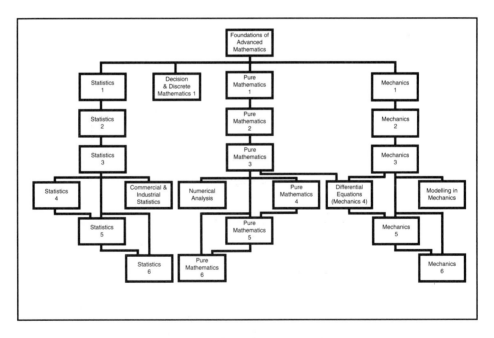

This is one of the series of books written to support the course. Its position within the whole scheme can be seen in the diagram above.

Mathematics in Education and Industry is a curriculum development body which aims to promote the links between Education and Industry in Mathematics and to produce relevant examination and teaching syllabuses and support material. Since its foundation in the 1960s, MEI has provided syllabuses for GCSE (or O Level), Additional Mathematics and A Level.

For more information about MEI Structured Mathematics or other syllabuses and materials, write to MEI Office, 11 Market Place, Bradford on Avon, BA15 1LL.

Introduction

This book has been written specifically to meet the needs of students following the Decision and Discrete Mathematics Component of MEI Structured Mathematics. The text includes a number of routine exercises, to which the answers are given. It is envisaged that you will work through most of these. In addition, there are many suggestions for investigations. A selection of these together with other ideas of your own will give individuality to your folder of work. Some of the investigations could develop into coursework tasks, four of which are required for assessment as detailed in the *Guidelines and Syllabus* booklet. A bank of coursework tasks is also available from the MEI office.

Algorithms are used so extensively in Decision and Discrete Mathematics that they are the subject of the opening chapter of this book. In this chapter, you are introduced to the questions

What are algorithms?

How do we communicate algorithms?

How do we measure the efficiency of algorithms?

However, since algorithms form an extensive area of study in their own right, their treatment is not developed vigorously here.

Although the syllabus for this Component does not specifically require the use of computers or of programming languages, it would be wrong to deny yourself this avenue of enquiry. The book steers a middle course: it provides sufficient breadth of material for you to follow your own inclination and expertise in this matter. If you have a computing background, or are following a parallel course in computer programming, you will benefit from making use of this.

If you do not have a computing background, but still want to explore this dimension, you can use computer packages if they are available (in some chapters this is a particularly appropriate approach), or you can use the computer programmes in the book 'blind'. The choice of languages is intended to be accessible to as wide an audience as possible, but do substitute your favourite programming language if it is not included.

The authors would like to thank Peter Butt of the City of London School for his help and ideas, particularly in the first two chapters of the book.

Chris Compton and Geoff Rigby

Contents

Algorithms

Monday's child is fair of face,
Tuesday's child is full of grace,
Wednesday's child is full of woe,
Thursday's child has far to go,
Friday's child is loving and giving,
Saturday's child works hard for its living,
And a child that is born on the Sabbath day,
Is fair and wise and good and gay.

Do you know on which day of the week you were born? If not, then you could use Zeller's Algorithm to work it out from your date of birth. An algorithm is simply a sequence of precise instructions to solve a problem.

Zeller's Algorithm

Let day number = D,
month number = M,
and year = Y.

If M is 1 or 2 add 12 to M and subtract 1 from Y.

Let C be the first two digits of Y and Y' be the last two digits of Y.

Add together the integer parts of $(2.6M - 5.39)$, $(Y'/4)$ and $(C/4)$, then add on D and Y' and subtract 2C. (Integer part of 2.3 is 2, of 6.7 is 6, i.e. the whole number part, but note that integer part of -1.7 is -2 and -3.1 is -4 etc.)

Find the remainder when this quantity is divided by 7.

If remainder is 0 the day was a Sunday, if it is 1 a Monday etc.

Example: May 15, 1991

D = 15
M = 5
Y = 1991

C = 19
Y' = 91

$7 + 22 + 4 + 15 + 91 - 38 = 101$

3

∴ May 15, 1991 was a Wednesday

Try Zeller's Algorithm for yourself using your own date of birth.

Many algorithms are rather tedious to work through by hand, and can be written in such a way that a computer can carry out the task for us. It is helpful, therefore, to become familiar with some computer programming language. Zeller's Algorithm could be written in BBC Basic as follows.

```
10  INPUT  "Date of birth ( eg 4,11,1965 )"; D,M,Y
20  IF M < 3 THEN M= M + 12 : Y = Y - 1
30  C = INT(Y / 100)
40  Y1 = Y - 100 * C
50  S = INT(2.6 * M - 5.39) + INT(Y1 / 4) + INT(C / 4) + D + Y1 - 2 * C
60  DAY = S - 7 * INT(S / 7)
70 PRINT DAY
```

If you have done some programming before you can see that this will just print out the day number, not its name. You might like to add some statements to get the output as a day of the week rather than a number.

You will have been using algorithms since you first went to school. The algorithms that you were taught for long multiplication and division would result in working like this:

$$
\begin{array}{r}
163 \\
\times 24 \\
\hline
3260 \\
652 \\
\hline
3912
\end{array}
\qquad\qquad
\begin{array}{r}
163 \\
24\,\overline{)3912} \\
24 \\
\hline
151 \\
144 \\
\hline
72 \\
72 \\
\hline
0
\end{array}
$$

The multiplication algorithm involves such instructions as:
write down a 0;
multiply the top row by the tens digit; etc.
It is a challenging exercise to write down precise instructions for these two algorithms: we have become so used to using them that we do so without really thinking.

The word 'algorithm' has become more commonplace since the development of the computer. A computer program is simply an algorithm written in such a way that a machine can carry it out. Our interest in this course is in mathematical algorithms, but cookery recipes, knitting patterns and instructions for setting the video to record your favourite TV programme could all be said to be algorithms. People, like machines, can work through algorithms automatically and can be led to the solution of a problem without needing to understand the process. Try writing a set of instructions to enable an eleven year old, who knows nothing of algebra, to solve a pair of simultaneous equations.

Communicating an Algorithm

How do we communicate our algorithms? In Zeller's Algorithm we used ordinary language and the computer language BBC Basic. The form of communication we choose depends on to whom (child, scientist etc.) or to what (computer, programmable calculator) we are trying to convey the algorithm. In all cases we must consider both the language we use and the nature of the steps into which we break the process down.

Let us take as an example an algorithm to find the real roots of the quadratic equation

$$ax^2 + bx + c = 0 \qquad \text{(assume } a \neq 0\text{)}$$

using the formula

$$x = \frac{-b \pm \sqrt{b^2 - 4ac}}{2a}$$

Using *pseudo-computer code* (a sort of stylised English) we could write

calculate $b^2 - 4ac$; note its value;
  if this value is negative [no real roots – stop]
    else   [calculate root of value
                         calculate $(-b + \text{root})/(2a)$
                         calculate $(-b - \text{root})/(2a)$
                         stop] .

For a programmable calculator we could write the following instructions.

Casio Graphic	Texas Instruments TI-81
$? \to A$	:Input A
$? \to B$	:Input B
$? \to C$	:Input C
$\sqrt{B^2 - 4AC} \to D$	$:\sqrt{B^2 - 4AC} \to D$
$(-B + D) \div (2A)$	$:(-B + D) \div (2A)$
◢	:Pause
$(-B - D) \div (2A)$	$:(-B - D) \div (2A)$

Note that these instructions assume real roots, since there is no test to check if the roots are real.

In BBC Basic computer programming language we could write the following program.

```
10 INPUT "A, B, C"; A ,B ,C
20 D = B * B - 4*A*C
30 IF D < 0 THEN PRINT "No real roots":STOP
40 PRINT (- B + SQR(D))/(2 * A)
50 PRINT (- B - SQR(D))/(2 * A)
```

Another common method of communicating the steps in an algorithm is to use a *flowchart*. A flowchart is a diagrammatic representation of the sequence of steps in an algorithm. It can be particularly helpful in showing the structure where there are large numbers of conditional statements involved.

For our quadratic equation example the flowchart would look like the one in figure 1.1.

Often a process can be broken down into a number of smaller processes, and those into smaller ones still, and so on. Instead of one large algorithm the process becomes a number of smaller ones. The relationship between these can be shown in a *structure diagram*. You might have used the programming language LOGO to draw pictures on the computer screen. Many computer languages, including LOGO, are designed to execute algorithms written in this structured way.

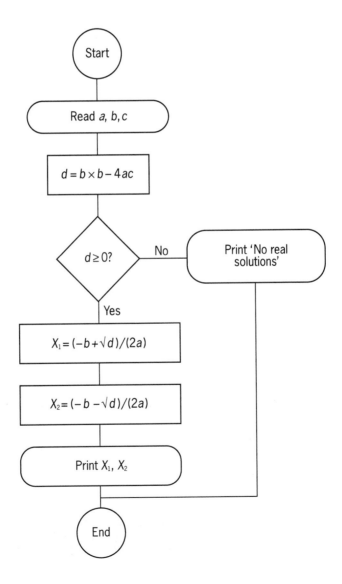

Figure 1.1

Suppose you wanted to draw the train shown in figure 1.2.

Figure 1.2

The train is made up of an ENGINE and TRUCKS.

The ENGINE is made up of a TRUCK with a CAB and FUNNEL (figure 1.3).

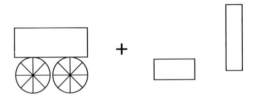

Figure 1.3

A TRUCK is made up of a BLOCK and WHEELS (figure 1.4).

Figure 1.4

A WHEEL is made up if a STAR and CIRCLE (figure 1.5)

Figure 1.5

We can illustrate this with the structure diagram shown in figure 1.6.

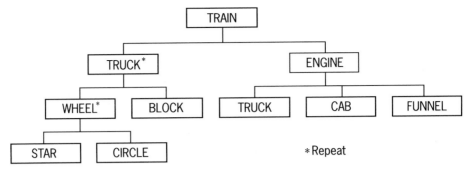

Figure 1.6

You would begin by writing procedures to draw a circle and a star. Your procedure for a wheel would then make use of these two procedures. By the time you had worked your way up the structure diagram, the instruction to draw a train would simply be TRAIN.

The program for TRAIN would be

TRUCK
TRUCK
ENGINE

The program for TRUCK would be

WHEEL
WHEEL
BLOCK

And so on. The actual LOGO commands (like 'FD 200') would only come in the lowest level procedures.

The one procedure missing from this analysis is the COUPLING. Where would this fit into the structure diagram?

Below are two algorithms, one expressed in pseudo-code and the other as a flowchart. Consider representing them differently, defining the target user for whom (or which) each representation would be suitable.

Russian peasants' algorithm for long multiplication
Write down side by side the two numbers to be multiplied.
Repeatedly [beneath the left hand number, write down the number
which is half the number above, ignoring any remainder,
and beneath the right hand number, write down the number
which is double the number above]
until you reach the row when the number in the halving column is 1.
Delete those rows where the number in the halving column is a multiple of 2.
Add up those numbers still left in the doubling column.
This number is the result of multiplying the two original numbers.

Here is an example.

$$
\begin{array}{cc}
163 & 24 \\
81 & 48 \\
\cancel{40} & \cancel{96} \\
\cancel{20} & \cancel{192} \\
\cancel{10} & \cancel{384} \\
5 & 768 \\
\cancel{2} & \cancel{1536} \\
1 & 3072 \\
\hline
& 3912 \\
\hline
\end{array}
$$

Euclid's method for finding the highest common factor (H.C.F.) of two integers x and y
(i.e. the largest integer that will divide into both x and y)
The method is described in the flowchart in figure 1.7.

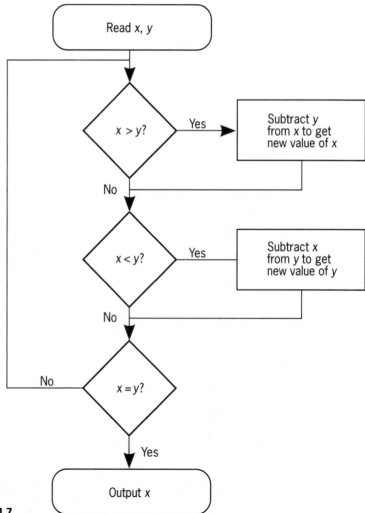

Figure 1.7

If you try the flowchart with $x = 24$ and $y = 32$, you should get the output 8, which is the H.C.F. of 24 and 32.

Efficiency

Most problems can be solved using a variety of algorithms, some of which might be more *efficient* than others. By efficient we usually mean quicker, but there might be other considerations too. For example if the algorithm needs to be run on a computer, we will want to know how much storage capacity it needs.

As a simple example of improving efficiency, consider again the algorithm to find the real roots of the quadratic equation

$$ax^2 + bx + c = 0$$

using the formula

$$x = \frac{-b \pm \sqrt{b^2 - 4ac}}{2a}$$

It is a good idea to calculate the value of $b^2 - 4ac$ as a first step, because the sign of that value has to be checked to see whether it is worth going on with the calculation. If it is, the value $b^2 - 4ac$ has to be used twice in the calculation.

If an algorithm requires the evaluation of a quadratic expression, the way in which the expression is written can make a difference to efficiency.

e.g $\qquad\qquad\qquad\qquad x^2 + 2x + 9 \qquad\qquad\qquad\qquad$ ①

can be written as $\qquad\qquad x(x + 2) + 9 \qquad\qquad\qquad\qquad$ ②

Check for yourself that the two expressions are equivalent.

When $x = 5$, evaluation with a calculator requires the following entries:

using ① $\qquad\qquad\quad$ ⑤ⓧ⑤⊞②ⓧ⑤⊞⑨⊟ $\qquad$ 10 steps

using ② $\qquad\qquad\quad$ ⑤⊞②⊟ⓧ⑤⊞⑨⊟ $\qquad$ 9 steps.

Now investigate $x^3 + 2x^2 + 3x + 9$ when $x = 5$.
(Assume that x^3 will be calculated as $x{\cdot}x{\cdot}x$)

Often the ordering of the conditional steps (referred to as *cascading*) in an algorithm can lead to differences in efficiency. Most instruction booklets contain 'trouble shooting guides' explaining what to do if your video won't work, your car won't start and so on. These checklists are organised in such a way that you look for the most common faults first.

Figure 1.8 gives an algorithm in the form of a flowchart to test if a two digit number is prime. Try it as it stands and then investigate whether a change in the order of the tests would lead to a more efficient algorithm.

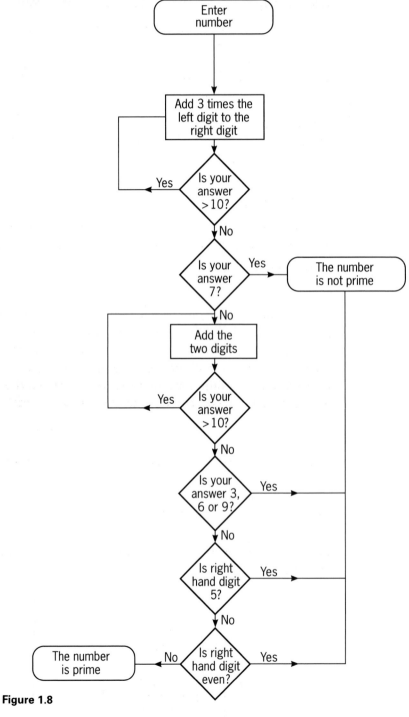

Figure 1.8

Recurrence Relations

Activity

Work through this algorithm, starting with the word 'mathematics'.

Step 1   Think of an English word and write it down.
Step 2   Write, as a word, the number of letters in the word you have just written.
Step 3   If the last two words you have written down are the same, stop.
Step 4   Go back to step 2.

Repeat this for several different words. Do you always get the same answer? What happens if you do it in French? Or in other languages like Spanish or Welsh?

Iteration

In the activity above you will have produced a sequence of answers, each of which became the starting point for the next run through:

mathematics $\rightarrow$ eleven $\rightarrow$ six $\rightarrow$ three $\rightarrow$ . . . . . .

This type of algorithm is called an *iteration*.

In this case the algorithm is given as a sequence of numbered instructions, rather like a Basic program, except that it is written in English. This is not the only way of writing an iteration, or indeed the most common. In mathematical examples the algorithm for an iteration is often written in the form of a *recurrence relation*, the rule for going from one term to the next. You also need to know the first term so you can get started.

Here is an example of an iteration given as a recurrence relation:

$$x_{n+1} = \frac{x_n^2 + 9}{2x_n} \qquad \text{with starting value} \quad x_0 = 1$$

Working through this, the iteration proceeds as follows, to calculator accuracy.

$$x_0 = 1$$

$$x_1 = \frac{1^2 + 9}{2} = 5$$

$$x_2 = \frac{5^2 + 9}{2 \times 5} = 3.4$$

$$x_3 = \frac{3.4^2 + 9}{2 \times 3.4} = 3.023\ 529\ 4$$

$$x_4 = \frac{3.023\ 529\ 4^2 + 9}{2 \times 3.023\ 529\ 4} = 3.000\ 091\ 6$$

$$x_5 = \frac{3.000\ 091\ 6^2 + 9}{2 \times 3.000\ 091\ 6} = 3$$

$$x_6 = \frac{3^2 + 9}{2 \times 3} = 3$$

Work through this algorithm again, this time replacing the number 9 on the top line by 25. What do you think is happening? Does the starting value, x_0, make any difference to the final outcome? What happens if you change 9 to a negative number, say -4?

An unusual way of working out π is to use Wallis's Product:

$$\pi = 2 \times \frac{4}{3} \times \frac{16}{15} \times \frac{36}{35} \times \frac{64}{63} \times \ldots \ldots$$

You can write the algorithm for this as the iteration

$$x_{n+1} = x_n \times \left[\frac{4n^2}{4n^2 - 1} \right] \quad : \quad x_0 = 2$$

A recurrence relation may involve more than one term, like this one which generates the Fibonacci sequence: 1, 1, 2, 3, 5, 8, 13, $\ldots \ldots$

$$x_{n+2} = x_{n+1} + x_n : \quad x_0 = 1,\ x_1 = 1$$

The important thing to notice in these two examples is that after each run through you have a specific value to use as the starting point for the next run through. This is always the case in an iterative process.

Recursion

Bigger fleas have little fleas upon their backs to bite 'em
And little fleas have littler fleas and so ad infinitum.

Sometimes the calculation using a recurrence relation can be carried out in two different ways. Suppose you wanted to find x_6 in this example:

$$x_{n+1} = (n + 1)x_n : \quad x_0 = 1.$$

You could work it from the bottom up as follows.

$$1 \rightarrow 1 \rightarrow 2 \rightarrow 6 \rightarrow 24 \rightarrow 120 \rightarrow 720$$
$$x_0 \quad x_1 \quad x_2 \quad x_3 \quad x_4 \quad x_5 \quad x_6$$

Or you could work it from the top down as follows.

$$x_6 = 6x_5 = 30x_4 = 120x_3 = 360x_2 = 720x_1 = 720x_0 = 720 \text{ (since } x_0 = 1)$$

The answer of course is the same both ways.

The first approach is an iteration, since at each stage we have a specific value to use as the starting point for the next calculation. The second approach is called recursion. When we use this method, we do not have a specific value to work with until we arrive at a final answer: until then, it is always defined in terms of the next step. If you are doing this calculation by hand, the difference between the two methods may seem trivial, but if you are a computer programmer the two methods lead to fundamentally different styles of program, so the difference is crucial.

The essential feature of recursion is that the solution to a problem is described in terms of solutions to easier or smaller versions of the same problem. You will have realised that in the example above you were finding 6!, factorial (6). In the recursive method you did this by using

factorial (6) = 6 × factorial (5)
factorial (5) = 5 × factorial (4) and so on.

The solution to finding factorial (6) was given in terms of finding factorial (5), a slightly easier version of the same problem, and so on all the way down to factorial (0) which you were given to be 1.

Here are some more non-mathematical examples of recursion, starting with a well known story.

It was a dark and stormy night. The wind howled, and rain lashed the rattling window panes. Three children sat huddled over the embers of a dying fire. The youngest one said, "Tell us a story". The oldest one replied:

"It was a dark and stormy night. The wind howled, and rain lashed the rattling window panes. Three children sat huddled over the embers of a dying fire. The youngest one said, "Tell us a story". The oldest one replied:

"It was a dark and stormy night. . . . . . ." and so on.

You can write this as a structured program, in LOGO, called STORY. Notice how the program refers to itself at the end of the second line.

TO STORY
PRINT "It was a dark . . . The oldest one replied:" STORY
END

NOTE

This is not a very good program because it goes on for ever, calling itself up time and time again. Like most recurrence relations, it should have a stopping condition built in for otherwise it never leads us to an 'answer'. The same is true of the next example.

A dictionary definition: **Recursion** *see Recursion.*

Heuristic Algorithms

The Bin Packing Problem

You are faced with the problem of fitting a number of boxes of the same width and depth but different heights into a rack. The rack is the same depth as the boxes. It is divided into slots of the same width and of a fixed height as shown in figure 1.9.

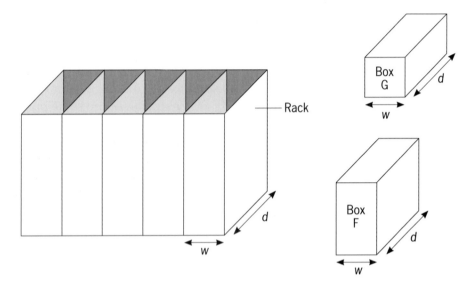

Figure 1.9

There are 11 boxes, A to K, with heights (in dm) as follows.

A	B	C	D	E	F	G	H	I	J	K
8	7	4	9	6	9	5	5	6	7	8

The rack is 15 dm high and you are to stack the boxes one on top of the other using as few slots as possible.

Similar problems might be cutting lengths of wood from standard length planks, or fitting vehicles into lanes on a car ferry. In each case we are trying to make best possible use of the space available and avoid waste in the form of unused space in the racks, offcuts of wood and unfilled lanes on the ferry.

You can solve all of these problems by a process of trial and error and you will probably have no trouble coming up with the best answer (usually referred to as the optimal solution). However, solving a large problem of this type isn't so easy. It is worth looking for a more systematic approach to finding the best answer, particularly one that could be carried out by a computer. In subsequent chapters we shall be looking at a number of other problems that require development of computer algorithms if large amounts of data are to be handled.

For the bin packing problem there is actually no known algorithm that will *always* produce the best (or optimal) solution. There are many algorithms that attempt to find a good solution: these are called *heuristic algorithms* and we shall meet them again in the chapter on the travelling salesman problem. This raises another issue in our discussion of what constitutes an efficient algorithm. Since we cannot guarantee getting the best solution, if we are choosing from a range of algorithms we would want one that most consistently gave better solutions than the others. The consistency with which an algorithm gives a good solution is therefore another factor in its efficiency.

Exercise 1A

1. Try to find the best solution to the bin packing problem above by trial and error. What is the minimum number of slots that is required? This would be referred to as a lower bound for the solution.
2. Did you adopt any specific strategy to solve the problem, and if so could you turn it into an algorithm? Try to write your method down such that an eleven-year-old could follow it.
3. How much wasted space is there in your solution?

Investigation

Here are three heuristic algorithms for you to try out. You will need to apply the algorithms to a variety of examples to be able to form a judgement about their relative efficiency, so use them first on the bin packing problem then on the plumbing, ferry loading and disc storage problems given below.

a) **Full-bin algorithm.**
Look for combinations of boxes to fill bins. Pack these boxes. For the remainder, place the next box to be packed in the first available slot that can take that box.

b) **First-fit algorithm.**
Taking the boxes in the order listed, place the next box to be packed in the first available slot that can take that box.

c) **First-fit decreasing algorithm.**
(i) Reorder the boxes in order of decreasing size.
(ii) Apply the first-fit algorithm to this reordered list.

The Plumbing Problem

A plumber is using lengths of pipe 12 feet long and wishes to cut the following lengths

Length (ft)	Number
2	2
3	4
4	3
6	1
7	2

What is the best way of achieving this so that he wastes as little pipe as possible?

The Ferry Loading Problem

A small car-ferry has 4 lanes, each 20 m long. The following vehicles are waiting to be loaded.

Petrol tanker	14 m	Car and trailer	8 m
Car	4 m	Car	3 m
Range Rover	5 m	Coach	12 m
Car	4 m	Lorry	11 m
Car	3 m	Car	4 m
Van	4 m	Lorry	10 m

Can all these vehicles be taken on one trip?

The Disc Storage Problem

A software manufacturer wants to fit the following computer programs on to four 400 kbyte discs.

Program	A	B	C	D	E	F	G	H	I	J
Size (kbytes)	100	80	60	65	110	25	50	60	90	140

Program	K	L	M	N	O	P	Q	R
Size (kbytes)	75	120	75	100	70	200	120	40

Can this be done?

Which algorithm have you found to be the most efficient?
Which one do you think would be easiest to automate, and why?

You have probably been drawing diagrams or possibly working with cut-out shapes. The following is a computational procedure that you could use for the first-fit or first-fit decreasing algorithms.

Define a list of numbers, P, for the heights of the packages (ordered if necessary).

For the bin-packing example, P = {8, 7, 4, 9, 6, 9, 5, 5, 6, 7, 8}

Define a second set of numbers, B, for the space remaining in the bins. At the very worst this list will need to be as long as the list of packages. For this example B = {15, 15, 15, 15, 15, 15, ...} initially.

Now follow the steps described below.

Step 1	Take the first entry in P.	
Step 2	Is it less than or equal to the first entry in B?	Yes → Step 4 No → Step 3
Step 3	Go to next B entry. Is it less than or equal to this entry in B?	Yes → Step 4 No → Step 3
Step 4	Reduce the B entry by this amount.	
Step 5	Any more entries in P?	Yes → Take next entry in P, go to Step 2 No → Stop

The result of applying this algorithm is shown below.

$$P = \{8, 7, 4, 9, 6, 9, 5, 5, 6, 7, 8\}$$
$$B = \{15, 15, 15, 15, 15, 15, ...\}$$
$$7 \quad 11 \quad 9 \quad 10 \quad 9 \quad 7$$
$$0 \quad 2 \quad 0 \quad 5 \quad 2$$

It is easy to see how many bins are used, how much free space there is in each and what packages are in each bin. It is a fairly easy task from here to produce a computer program to automate the process.

Exercise 1B

1. Construct a flowchart to clarify whether a married woman has reached an age at which she is eligible for a pension. The regulations are as follows.

   The earliest date on which a woman can draw a retirement pension is 60.
   On her own insurance she can get a pension if she has already retired from regular employment. If not, she must wait until she retires or reaches the age of 65.
   At the age of 65 the pension is paid irrespective of retirement.
   On her husband's insurance, however, she cannot get a pension until he has reached the age of 65 and retired from regular employment, or until he is 70 if he does not retire before that age.

2. An algorithm to find the date of Easter Sunday for any year from 1900 to 2000 is as follows:
   (i) Let a be the remainder when the number of the year is divided by 4.
   (ii) Let b be the remainder when it is divided by 7.
   (iii) Let c be the remainder when it is divided by 19.
   (iv) Let d be the remainder when $19c + 24$ is divided by 30.
   (v) Let e be the remainder when $2a + 4b + 6d + 5$ is divided by 7.
   (vi) Easter Sunday is the $(22 + d + e)$th day of March or the $(d + e - 9)$th day of April, depending which of these two quantities gives a valid date. Consider other ways of expressing this algorithm, e.g. flowchart or computer program, and test its accuracy by applying it to years for which you know the date of Easter.

3. Given below is a table used in an algorithm for converting Roman to decimal numbers.

	M	D	C	L	X	V	I
1	1000/2	500/3	100/9	50/5	10/10	5/7	1/11
2	1000/2	500/3	100/9	50/5	10/10	5/7	1/11
3			100/9	50/5	10/10	5/7	1/11
4			100/4	50/5	10/10	5/7	1/11
5				50/6	10/10	5/7	1/11
6					10/6	5/7	1/11
7						5/8	1/11
8							1/8
9	800/5	300/5	100/4	50/6	10/10	5/8	1/11
10			80/7	30/7	10/6	5/8	1/11
11					8/0	3/0	1/8

Take the Roman CIX as an example.
Always start by looking at row 1. Look at the row 1 entry in the column headed C (the first symbol in this Roman Number) to find 100/9. This means add 100 into a running total and move to row 9.

Take the second symbol I and look down column I to row 9. You find 1/11, so add 1 to the running total to give 101 and move to row 11. Finally look down column X to row 11 where you find 8/0, so add 8 to the running total to give 109. Since this was the last symbol in the number, we have finished and CIX = 109. (If you end up in a blank square you have made an error.)

Consider writing the algorithm in various ways and use it to carry out some conversions from Roman to decimal numbers. Does the algorithm have any limitations?
Can you write an algorithm to convert decimal to Roman numbers?

4. Computer programming languages contain statements that perform repetitions. In BBC Basic the 'for. . . .next' statement works as follows.

```
FOR I = 1 TO 3          FOR I = 1 TO 2
PRINT I                 FOR J = 1 TO 2
NEXT I                  PRINT I,J
                        NEXT J
                        NEXT I
```

The resulting printouts will be as follows.

```
1                       1 1
2                       1 2
3                       2 1
                        2 2
```

In a certain town the bus tickets are numbered 0000 to 9999, and children collect those whose digits add up to 21. How many will there be in a sequence of tickets from 0000 to 9999?

Two algorithms to solve the problem are written in BBC Basic below. Show that each achieves the desired result and compare their efficiency by counting the number of additions/subtractions and comparisons. (Note: It is not essential that this question be tackled on a computer.)

```
TOTAL = 0                          TOTAL = 0 : SUM = 0
FOR I = 0 TO 9                     FOR I = 0 TO 9
FOR J = 0 TO 9                     FOR J = 0 TO 9
FOR K = 0 TO 9                     FOR K = 0 TO 9
FOR L = 0 TO 9                     FOR L = 0 TO 9
SUM = I + J + K + L                IF SUM = 21 THEN TOTAL = TOTAL + 1
IF SUM = 21 THEN TOTAL = TOTAL + 1 SUM = SUM + 1
NEXT L                             NEXT L
NEXT K                             SUM = SUM - 8
NEXT J                             NEXT K
PRINT TOTAL                        SUM = SUM-8
                                   NEXT J
                                   SUM = SUM - 8
                                   NEXT I
                                   PRINT TOTAL
```

Computer Activities

1. Use Zeller's Algorithm to show that the 13th of the month is marginally more likely to be a Friday than any other day of the week. The days of the week sequence repeats itself over a 400 year cycle (century years are only leap years if divisible by 400), so consider the 13th of every month from, say, January 1901 to December 2300. Produce a frequency table for the number of occurrences of each day of the week.

2. All books have an ISBN (International Standard Book Number) of 10 digits. The last is a check digit produced by performing a calculation on the other nine. Its purpose is to reduce the likelihood of copying down a wrong number. The check digit is found by multiplying the first digit by 1, the second by 2, the third by 3 and so on up to the ninth, and adding the results, then finding the remainder when this sum is divided by eleven. If the remainder is 0 to 9 this digit is the check digit and if the remainder is 10 an X is used as the check digit.

   e.g.   019281022 gives
   $$0 \times 1 + 1 \times 2 + 9 \times 3 + 2 \times 4 + 8 \times 5 + 1 \times 6 + 0 \times 7 + 2 \times 8 + 2 \times 9$$
   sum $= 117$
   remainder when divided by 11 is 7
   So the full 10 digit number is 019 281 022 7

   Write a computer program to perform this algorithm and check it on some ISBNs.

Investigations

1. Write an algorithm to find all the divisors of an integer.

   e.g. the divisors of 24 are 1, 2, 3, 4, 6, 8, 12, 24.

   A 'perfect' number is one that is equal to the sum of all its divisors that are less than itself.
   The first perfect number is 6 since $6 = 1 + 2 + 3$.
   Write an algorithm to find perfect numbers and use it to find the next two perfect numbers. (One if you're working manually!)

Algorithms

2. The Knapsack Problem.

A hiker going on a camping trip can carry a weight of up to 45 pounds in his knapsack. There are five items that he had hoped to take but to take them all would exceed his weight allowance. He has assigned a value to each item. The items and their weights and values are as follows:

Item	Weight	Value
1	18	27
2	12	9
3	15	30
4	16	16
5	13	7

What items should he pack so that their total value is a maximum, subject to the weight restriction?

Solve the problem by trial and error and also suggest and test heuristic algorithms that would be useful for larger problems of this type.

3. Below is a diagram of the Hampton Court Maze. Write an algorithm to assist people in finding their way to the centre. Your algorithm should be general, so try it out on other mazes.

(*The Spode Group's* **Decision Maths Pack***, available from Hodder and Stoughton, has some useful material on mazes.*)

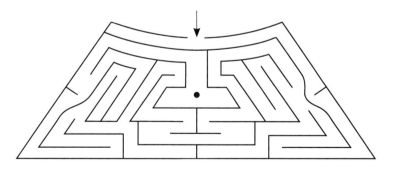

Figure 1.10

4. You may have come across Pascal's Triangle

$$
\begin{array}{ccccccc}
 & & & 1 & & & \\
 & & 1 & & 1 & & \\
 & 1 & & 2 & & 1 & \\
1 & & 3 & & 3 & & 1
\end{array}
$$

etc.

For convenience, number the rows 1, 2 etc. and label the entries in each row as the 1st, 2nd etc. Thus the third row is 1   2   1 and its 2nd entry is 2.

Here are three ways in which the numbers in the triangle can be produced.

(i)   Each new entry is the sum of the two numbers immediately above it.

$$
\begin{array}{ccc}
1 & & 2 \\
 & 3 &
\end{array}
$$

(ii)   The rth entry in row n is given by the formula

$$\frac{(n-1)!}{(r-1)!(n-r)!}$$

e.g. row 3, 2nd entry $= \dfrac{2!}{1!1!} = 2$

(iii)   Row n has   1st entry always 1

$$2\text{nd entry} = \frac{n-1}{1} \times 1\text{st entry}$$

$$3\text{rd entry} = \frac{n-2}{2} \times 2\text{nd entry}$$

and so on up to

$$(r+1)\text{th entry} = \frac{n-r}{r} \times r\text{th entry}$$

e.g. row 3   1st entry $= 1$

$$2\text{nd entry} = \frac{2}{1} \times 1 = 2$$

$$3\text{rd entry} = \frac{1}{2} \times 2 = 1$$

Write algorithms to produce Pascal's Triangle using the three different ideas and compare their efficiency.

KEY POINTS

- An algorithm is a well-defined, finite sequence of instructions used to solve a problem.
- Algorithms can be communicated in various ways, including

  Written English
  Pseudo-code
  Computer programming languages
  Flowcharts
  Structure Diagrams

- The efficiency of an algorithm is measured in terms of its speed of operation and its data storage requirements.
- You have now met some different types of algorithm, and should understand their main features. They are

  Iterative and recursive algorithms
  Heuristic algorithms.

Sorting and Searching

Sorting

Working with a partner, take a pack of 52 playing cards each and shuffle them thoroughly. Swap packs and sort the cards into suits in the order clubs, diamonds, hearts, spades, and within each suit from Ace up to King as quickly as you can.

Discuss how you went about sorting your cards, and compare your strategies. Try again using the same strategy, or try a different one.

Is a particular strategy always quicker?

Apart from strategy, what other factors will influence the time taken to sort the pack?

Another exercise you might like to try is to sort a set of weights into order when you are blindfolded.

Sorting is an everyday activity in which the efficiency of the algorithm used is very important. There are many sorting algorithms designed for use on computers, and there are computer packages available that enable you to compare the merits of the various algorithms. It is strongly recommended that you should use such a package. The Decision Maths Software produced by the Spode Group contains a suitable section on sorting: details are given in the introduction to that software.

We shall begin by looking at two methods of sorting a list of numbers into ascending order, and consider some of the features that you should take into account when comparing them. It should be borne in mind that what might seem an efficient method for a human being may not be so for a computer and vice versa. Both the number of items in the list to be sorted, and how muddled they are, affect the efficiency of the various algorithms.

Selection with Interchange Sort Algorithm

In this algorithm, the smallest number in the list is found and interchanged with the first number. Then the smallest number excluding the first is found and interchanged with the second number. Next the smallest number excluding the first two is found and interchanged with the third number. This process continues until the list is sorted.

To apply this to the list of eight numbers in figure 2.1, look through the whole list to find the smallest number, i.e. 1. Swap this with the 7 in the first position. The result after this first pass through the list is shown alongside.

Now look through the list from the second position downwards to find the smallest number, i.e. 2. Swap this with the 5 in the second position. The resulting list is marked '2nd pass'.

For a list of eight numbers, seven passes will be required before we can guarantee that the list is sorted. The results of the remaining passes are also shown in figure 2.1.

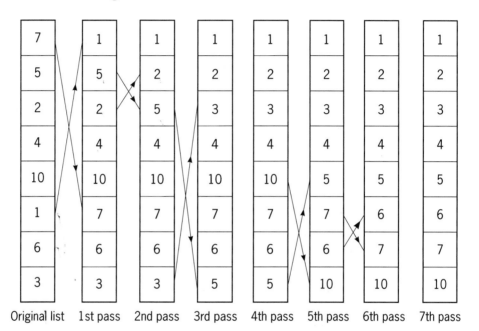

Original list   1st pass   2nd pass   3rd pass   4th pass   5th pass   6th pass   7th pass

Figure 2.1

NOTE

Although no interchanges take place on the 4th and 7th passes, this is a property of this particular list and the passes must still be carried out to ensure that the list is correctly sorted.

In order to see how this and other sorts can be performed by computer we need to introduce some notation.

Suppose we have the original list shown in figure 2.1.

We can write $L(1) = 7$, $L(2) = 5$ etc.. Thus the list is $L(i)$ where i goes from 1 to 8.

The algorithm can now be written as follows.
Look for smallest number in the list from $L(1)$ to $L(8)$, and swap it with $L(1)$.
Look for smallest number in the list from $L(2)$ to $L(8)$, and swap it with $L(2)$.
And so on.

In computer pseudo-code this would be

repeat with i = 1 to 7 [look for smallest number in the list from L(i) to L(8), and swap it with L(i)].

When comparing the efficiency of sorting algorithms, two useful measures are the number of comparisons and the number of swaps.

For the selection with Interchange Sort, you can see that:-
the number of comparisons on the
1st pass = 7
2nd pass = 6
3rd pass = 5
4th pass = 4
5th pass = 3
6th pass = 2
7th pass = 1.

This gives a total of $7 + 6 + 5 + 4 + 3 + 2 + 1 = 28$ comparisons.
The number of swaps will be at most one per pass, i.e. a maximum of 7.

How many comparisons and swaps would be required for a list of 10 numbers? Try to generalise to obtain formulae for the number of comparisons and swaps when the list is of length n.

Bubble Sort Algorithm

The bubble sort is so named because numbers which are below their correct positions tend to move up to their proper places, like bubbles in a glass of champagne. On the first pass, the first number in the list is compared with the second and whichever is smaller assumes the first position. The second number is then compared with the third and the smaller is placed in the second position, and so on through the list. At the end of the first pass the largest number will have moved to the bottom position.

For the second pass the process is repeated but excluding the last number, and on the third pass the last two numbers are excluded. The list is repeatedly processed in this way until no swaps take place in a pass. The list is then sorted.

Starting with the same original list as for the Selection with Interchange Sort (p.00) on the first pass we compare 5 and 7, and swap them; then 7 and 4, and swap them; then 7 and 10, and do not swap them; then 10 and 1, and swap them; then 10 and 6 and swap them, then finally 10 and 3 and swap them. This pass is shown in detail in figure 2.2. Note that the last number is now in its correct position.

The results after making the 2nd and subsequent passes are shown in figure 2.3. You should work through the process to check that you get these results.

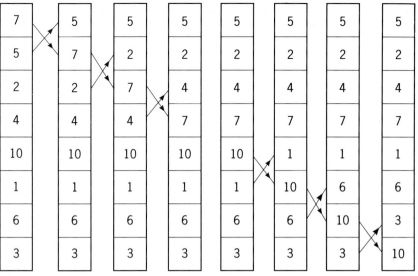

Figure 2.2   Original list   1st pass

Figure 2.3   2nd pass   3rd pass   4th pass   5th pass   6th pass   7th pass

The algorithm for the Bubble Sort for a list of length 8 can be written in computer pseudo-code like this:

repeat with $i = 1$ to 7
      [repeat with $j = 1$ to $(8 - i)$
      if $L(j) > L(j + 1)$ swap $L(j)$ and $L(j + 1)$]
if no swaps end repeat

The number of comparisons made in a Bubble Sort for a list of length 8 will be 7 on the first pass, 6 on the second pass etc.
If the maximum number of passes is needed, the total number of comparisons will be

$$7 + 6 + 5 + 4 + 3 + 2 + 1 = 28.$$

The number of swaps on the first pass will be anything up to 7; on the second, up to 6 etc.. So the maximum possible number of swaps will be

$$7 + 6 + 5 + 4 + 3 + 2 + 1 = 28.$$

How many comparisons and swaps would be required for a list of size 10? Try to generalise to obtain formulae for the number of comparisons and swaps when the list is of length n.

Exercise 2A

1. A common way of writing the date is to use a six digit number, the first two digits representing the day number, the next two representing the month and the last two representing the last two digits of the year number. Single digit days and months are padded out with leading zeros, thus September 4th 1991 becomes 040991. How would writing these date numbers in reverse (199040 for the example) be advantageous if you wanted to sort events in date order, or to rank a group of people in order of age?

2. Here are two programs in BBC Basic. They perform the Selection with Interchange Sort and the Bubble Sort, respectively. Investigate which is quicker for different sizes of data sets and varying levels of disorder.

```
FOR i = 1 TO n - 1
minpos = i
FOR j = i + 1 TO n
IF L(j)<L(minpos) THEN minpos = j
NEXT j
temp = L(i)
L(i) = L(minpos)
L(minpos) = temp
NEXT i
```

```
FOR i = 1 TO n - 1
swapflag = 0
FOR j = I TO n - i
IF L(j) > L(j + 1) THEN
temp = L(j)
L(j) = L(j + 1)
L(j + 1) = temp
swapflag = 1
NEXT j
IF swapflag = 0 THEN i = n - 1
NEXT i
```

The Input will be the same for both:

```
READ n
DIM L(n)
FOR i = 1 TO n : READ L(i) : NEXT i
DATA
```

where DATA is the value of n followed by the list of numbers to be sorted. Output can be achieved with:

```
FOR i = 1 TO n : PRINT L(i) : NEXT i
```

Computer Activity

1. As mentioned earlier, computer packages are available that enable you to compare sort algorithms. If you have access to one of these, this would be a good point at which to use it to explore other sort algorithms and carry out a more far reaching comparison of efficiency. You should be able to consider longer lists and different degrees of initial disorder, thus allowing you to draw more confident conclusions.

The Shuttle Sort Algorithm

1st pass: compare the first two numbers and swap if necessary.

2nd pass: compare the second and third numbers and swap if necessary, then compare first and second numbers and swap if necessary.

3rd pass: compare the third and fourth numbers and swap if necessary, then compare second and third numbers and swap if necessary and compare first and second numbers and swap if necessary.

And so on. The sequence is shown in figure 2.4.

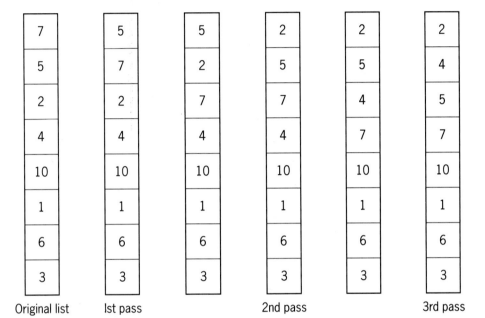

Original list   1st pass   2nd pass   3rd pass

Figure 2.4

Insertion Sort Algorithm

This is similar to the way you might arrange a hand of cards. Numbers are taken one at a time, in sequence, from the original list and inserted in their correct positions in a new list as shown in figure 2.5 (overleaf).

The Quick Sort Algorithm

To carry out the Quick Sort, first split the list into two sub-lists, one containing those numbers less than or equal to the first number in the list, the other containing those greater than the first number. Do not reorder the sub-lists. Place the first number between the two sub-lists. Repeat the process on sub-lists containing two or more numbers until there are no such sub-lists. The list is then sorted. The process is shown in figure 2.6 (overleaf).

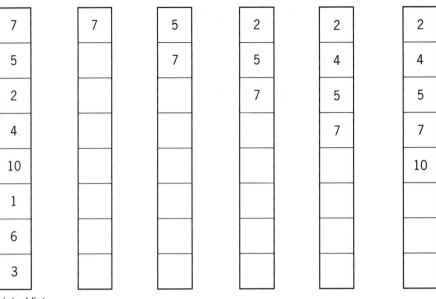

Original list

Figure 2.5

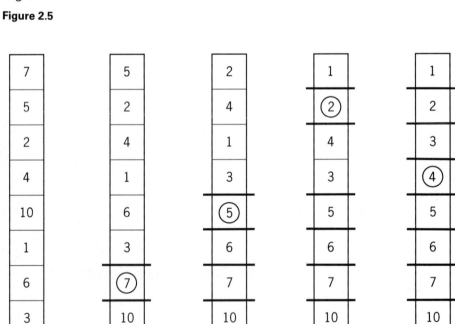

Original list

Figure 2.6

Investigation

1. Look carefully at the details of the Shuttle Sort, Insertion Sort and Quick Sort algorithms. Carry out the following investigation on them.
(i) Apply them to some lists of numbers (or words) to enable you to see clearly how they work.
(ii) Write the algorithms in either pseudo-code or some suitable

Investigation continued

programming language, and test them if you have access to a
computer.
(iii) Assess their efficiency by counting the number of comparisons
and swaps that will be involved. Try to obtain generalisations where
possible, and compare your results with those for the Selection with
Interchange Sort and the Bubble Sort algorithms.

Searching

Activities

1. Working in pairs, tell your partner to think of a whole number between
   1 and 99 (inclusive). Then by asking suitable questions to which the
   answer must be either yes or no, try to discover the number. The aim
   is to find the number by asking as few questions as possible. Swap
   over and let your partner try to find a number that you are thinking of.
   Repeat the exercise several times, trying different strategies. Discuss
   your strategies. What is the minimum, maximum and average number
   of questions required?

2. Treasure Island. (Again you will need a partner.)

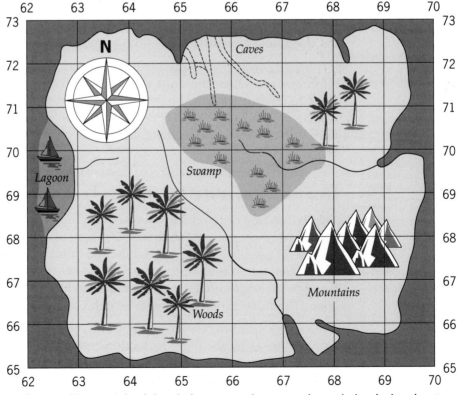

Somewhere on the island shown on the map above is buried a chest
of pirate treasure. Ask your partner to decide on the six-figure grid

reference of where it is hidden. You are allowed nine attempts at guessing the grid reference of the location of the treasure. After each attempt your partner will tell you if you need to go North or South and if you need to go East or West. Take it in turns to 'bury' the treasure and when you have played the game a few times discuss your strategies.

3. Use a dictionary or telephone directory to investigate how many items of data you look at when searching for a given word or someone's phone number. Compare various strategies and try to describe them as algorithms.

Searching, like sorting, is an everyday activity that has attracted a lot of attention from the writers of algorithms. In today's information-rich society, finding the item of data that you require can be like looking for a needle in a haystack. We shall consider three methods.

Linear Search Algorithm

This is the simplest of the search algorithms, in which you check each item of data in turn to see if it satisfies your criterion. There are no restrictions on the data, it will work even if the data is not ordered. It is, however, most inefficient. If the item for which you are looking is not there, you will still have checked every item of data. Imagine trying to find the name of a person, given their telephone number, by searching the telephone directory!

It is usually worth ordering the data in a way that suits your requirements. Often the same set of data will be ordered in different ways to facilitate different types of search request. For example, a library catalogue is ordered both according to author and according to book title. If the data is ordered there are two algorithms that we can consider using.

Index Sequential Search Algorithm

The data is first ordered and then subdivided. An extra list or index is then created containing the first or last item in each subdivision. Such a method is used in a dictionary where the index is positioned at the top right hand corner of the page. To find a given word, you first leaf through the pages, looking at the index, to locate the page that the word is on. Then you carry out a linear search on the selected page.

For a set of data held on a computer system you would need to create a sub-list. For example if you had a list of the S.T.D. codes for the U.K. ordered by town name, the sub-list could contain the position of the first town whose name began with A, B, C, ... etc. Thus to find York, the sub-list would first be searched to find Y. This would give the position from which to start the linear search of the main data.

Decision and Discrete Mathematics

Binary Search Algorithm

The data is first sorted into ascending order. The following steps are then carried out.

Step 1   Look at the middle item.
If this is the required item the search is finished.
If not, the item is in either the top or bottom half: decide which half by comparison with the middle item.

Step 2   Apply Step 1 to the chosen half.

At each stage the number of items to be searched is halved, hence the name of the algorithm.

The algorithm proceeds most smoothly when the number of data items is 3, 7, 15, 31, 63 etc. (i.e. of the form $2^n - 1$). Can you see why? What will be the maximum number of comparisons for each of these numbers of data items?

It can be worth adding dummy items to give a total of the form $2^n - 1$, but if this leads to adding a lot of extra items, it becomes preferable to adapt the algorithm to overcome the difficulty with the middle item.

Investigation

Investigate
(i)   the maximum number of comparisons per request
(ii) the mean number of comparisons per request

when searching a list of n items for a specific item of data using a linear search algorithm.

Repeat the investigation, this time for a binary search algorithm.

You may assume in each case that the list is sorted into ascending order. If you are unable to obtain general expressions, you should give results for a selection of values of n.

Exercise 2B

1. Using the notation $L(1) \ldots L(n)$ for the list of n items, write algorithms in either pseudo-code or a computer programming language for
   (a) The Linear search
   (b) The Binary search.
   If you have used a programming language and have access to a computer, test your results.

Exercise 2B continued

2. If you have access to large amount of data in computer form, e.g. a list of pupils in your school with their dates of birth, write an index sequential search algorithm to find individual pupils' dates of birth.

3. Suppose you wanted to write a computer program to play the number guessing game in the introductory exercise. What algorithm would you use to enable the computer to guess your number? Try to write a suitable program.

KEY POINTS

When you have read this chapter you should
- know that there are various types of sorting algorithm;
- understand that to compare their efficiency you need to consider
  (i) the number of comparisons
  (ii) the number of interchanges;
- understand that to compare the efficiency of two algorithms you must gather a lot of evidence, since you can only talk about average behaviour;
- be familiar with the main systematic searching methods: Linear, Index Sequential, and Binary;
- understand that the efficiency of these depends on the percentage of the data, on average, that needs to be examined before you find the item you want.

3 Finding the Shortest Path

Autoroute is a computerised route planner. You provide your starting point and destination and the computer prints out the best route together with directions, as you can see in this example. What method does such a program use?

```
                        AUTOROUTE V1.31

    ermediate route from Bolton Nr Manchester to Kirkbymoorside
    l time     :2 hrs
    l distance :107 miles
    +-----------------------------------+--------+---------+---+-----------------
    |                                   | Road   |   For   |Dir| Towards
    +-----------------------------------+--------+---------+---+-----------------
         DEPART Bolton                  |A673    |1/2 mile |E  |
         urn right onto                 |A666    |5 miles  |S  | Farnworth
       t M62 J15 turn left onto         |M62     |36 miles |E  | *Check access*
       : M62 J27 turn off onto          |M621    |3 miles  |E  | (M261 J1)
         M261 J1 turn off onto          |M261    |1/2 mile |E  | (M261 J2)
         M261 J2 turn off onto          |A643    |1 mile   |N  |
      .  Turn off onto                  |A58     |1/4 mile |NE | (A58(M))
    10:48|At A58(M) bear right onto      |A58(M)  |2 miles  |NE | Leeds
    10:50|At A58(M) turn off onto        |A61     |1/2 mile |N  | *Check access*
    10:51|Turn off onto                  |A58     |12 miles |NE | Wetherby
    11:09|Turn left onto                 |A1      |19 miles |NE | Ripon
    11:28|Turn off onto                  |A168    |8 miles  |E  | Thirsk
    11:37|Turn off onto                  |A170    |19 miles |E  | Scarborough
    12:00|ARRIVE Kirkbymoorside
    -----+-----------------------------+--------+---------+---+-----------------
```

Another technological innovation to help the motorist negotiate the traffic in a busy city is the 'in-car navigation system'. The motorist is in contact with a central computer which is constantly monitoring the state of traffic flow through a network of sensors in the city streets. The motorist simply keys his or her location and chosen destination into a small communication device located on the dashboard. The computer decides the best route based on the latest traffic information and transmits the necessary directions back to the driver at the appropriate moments. It keeps track of the car's progress using its network of sensors. A slightly simpler system, the Bosch Travelpilot, is already up and running in the major cities of the U.K.

As with *Autoroute*, at the heart of this system is an algorithm to find the shortest route between two points. Before we consider such an algorithm, try the following exercise based on a network representing the centre of a small town.

Exercise 3A

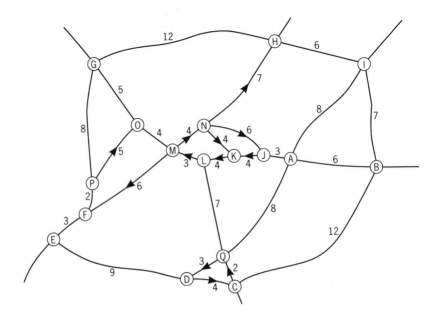

Junctions are represented by points or **nodes** and the roads by lines or **arcs**. The numbers on the arcs are the times in minutes that it takes to travel between the junctions. One-way streets are marked by arrows.

1. What are the quickest routes between the following places?
   (i)   From F to A
   (ii) from B to G
   (iii) from E to A
   (iv) from H to Q
   (v)   from N to C

2. (a) The fire station is located at the point C. Suppose there is a call to attend a fire at point G, what route should the fire engine take?
   (b) What would be the quickest way back to the station?

3. There has been a burglary at a shop at L. Police cars are located at points F, G and H when the alarm is raised, which one can get to the scene of the crime first?

4. Suppose it is decided that the road NK should be a traffic-free shopping precinct. What effect will this have on the quickest route from G to L?

5. What is the best route from the hospital at O to the point I where there has been a road accident?

6. What is the quickest route from J to N?
   Suppose there has been an accident in road KL blocking it. How long a delay would make it worth my while finding an alternative route?

7. The fire station is at C. Consider how you might approach the problem of deciding if it would be better at F.

Developing an algorithm for shortest route

In the network shown in figure 3.1 the numbers represent the lengths of the arcs. Find the shortest route from S to T.

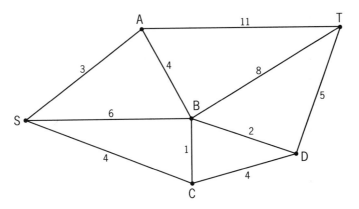

Figure 3.1

The solution to this problem can easily be found by inspection, but we want to develop a systematic approach that can be automated to apply to larger problems. Here is a possible procedure.

Label start node S with zero.
Consider those nodes that can be reached directly from S, in this case A, B and C. Put temporary labels on A, B, C equal to their direct distances from S, in this case 3, 6 and 4 respectively.
Select the node with the smallest temporary label (in this case A) and make its label permanent by putting a box around it. This indicates that the shortest distance from S to A is 3, and that it cannot be improved upon. Strictly the label on S is permanent and should have a box around it too, so at this stage we have the situation shown in figure 3.2.

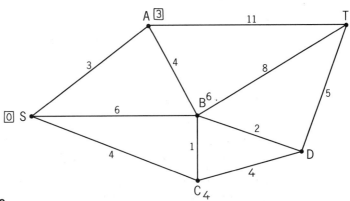

Figure 3.2

Consider all nodes that can be reached directly from A, in this case B and T.

The shortest route from S to B via A is $3 + 4 = 7$ (using the fact that we know the shortest route from S to A is 3). But B is already labelled with 6 (direct route from A) so we retain the 6 as the best so far.

The shortest route from S to T via A is $3 + 11 = 14$ so we put a temporary label of 14 on T.

The minimum temporary label is now 4 at node C. Make this permanent to indicate that the shortest route from S to C is 4 and that it cannot be improved upon. The situation is shown in figure 3.3.

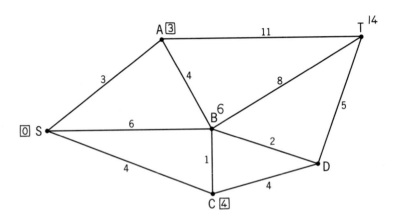

Figure 3.3

Consider all nodes that can be reached directly from C, in this case B and D.

The shortest route from S to B via C is $4 + 1 = 5$, which is shorter than the present label so we change the temporary label of B to 5.

The shortest route from S to D via C is $4 + 4 = 8$ so we put a temporary label of 8 on D.

The minimum temporary label is now 5 at node B. Make this permanent to indicate that the shortest route from S to B is 5 and that it cannot be improved upon. Figure 3.4 shows the stage that we have now reached.

Consider all nodes directly connected from B, i.e. D and T.

The shortest route from S to D via B is $5 + 2 = 7$, which is shorter than that on the present label, so we change it to 7.

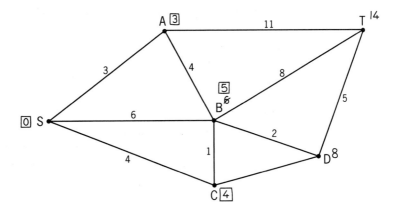

Figure 3.4

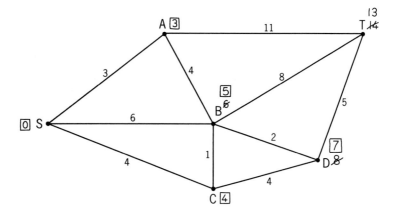

Figure 3.5

The shortest route from S to T via B is $5 + 8 = 13$, shorter than that on the present label so we change it to 13.

The minimum temporary label is now 7 at node D. Make this permanent to show that the shortest route from S to D is 7. Figure 3.5 shows the new situation.

Consider all nodes that can be reached directly from D, i.e. just T. Replace the label at T with $7 + 5 = 12$ since this is less than its present 13.

The minimum temporary label at node T is now 12. Make this permanent.

The destination node now has a permanent label as shown in figure 3.6, so we now know that the shortest route from S to T is 12. It remains only to find the route.

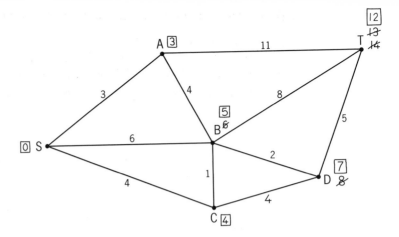

Figure 3.6

To find the shortest route we work backwards from T. The final stage brought us via D. If we look back through the working we will find that the best route to D was via B. It would have been a good idea to add to our labels the letter of the node from which we had found the best route. This would have saved us the trouble of looking back through our working. However, we can simply trace back through the network from T to S along arcs for which the difference in the permanent labels is equal to the arc lengths.

Thus we arrive at the optimum route S-C-B-D-T with a distance of 12, as shown in figure 3.7.

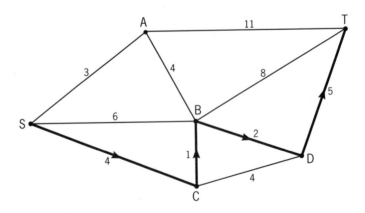

Figure 3.7

The algorithm that we have built up here was actually first described by Dijkstra, and has become known as *Dijkstra's Algorithm for the Shortest Route*. The steps in the algorithm are written in general form as follows.

Dijkstra's Algorithm for shortest route

Step 1   Label start node S with permanent label (P-label) of zero.
For all nodes that can be reached directly from S, assign
temporary labels (T-labels) equal to their direct distance from S.
Select the node with the smallest T-label and make its label
permanent.
The P-label represents the shortest distance from S to that node.

Step 2   Put a T-label on each node that can be reached directly from the
node that has just received a P-label. The T-label must be equal
to the sum of the P-label and the direct distance from it. If there
is an existing T-label at a node, it should be replaced only if the
new sum is smaller.
Select the minimum T-label and make it permanent.
If this labels the destination node go to step 3, otherwise repeat
Step 2.

Step 3   To find the shortest path(s), trace back from the destination
including any arc MN for which

P-label of M − P-label of N = length of arc MN

Exercise 3B

1. Use Dijkstra's algorithm to find the shortest path from S to T for the
networks (a), (b) and (c) below.

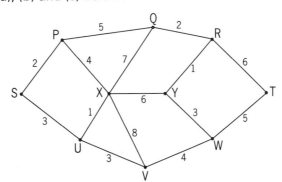

(a)

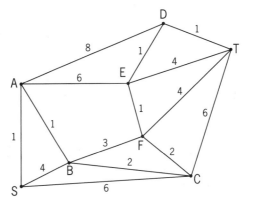

(b)

Exercise 3B continued

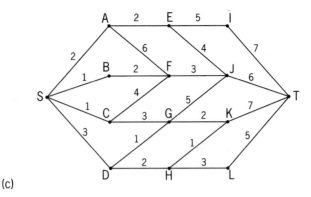

(c)

2. The map shows the main railway lines across the USA and gives the approximate times in hours for the various journeys.
   Find the quickest route

   (a) from Los Angeles to Chicago;
   (b) from New Orleans to Denver.

   If you can travel by road from El Paso to Santa Fe in 5 hours and from Santa Fe to Denver in 5 hours, would you save time on journey (a) or (b) by using a mix of road and rail? (You should neglect connection times.)

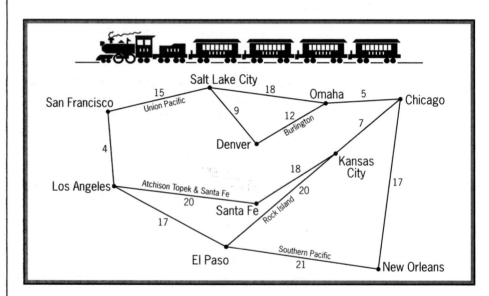

3. The fire department in Westingham has a team fighting a large blaze at one of the town's hotels. They urgently need extra help from one of the neighbouring towns, A, B or C. The estimated times (in minutes) to travel along the various sections of road from A, B and C to Westingham are shown on the network below. Which town's fire fighters should they call upon and how long will it take them to arrive at the fire?

Exercise 3B continued

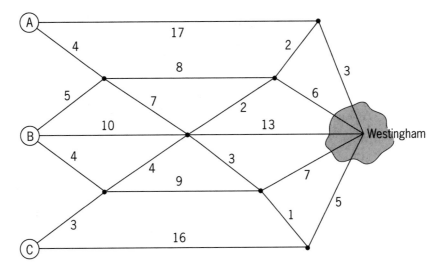

4. A company in the West Midlands has two factories, one in Kidderminster and the other in Cheltenham. A van has to travel regularly between the two factories. Use the map of the M5 between junctions 4 and 10 overleaf to answer the following questions. (The numbers on the arcs are the distances in miles and the numbers in italics against the circles are motorway junction numbers.)

(a) For the journey from Kidderminster to Cheltenham
   (i)   What is the shortest route?
   (ii) If we assume an average speed on the motorway of 60 mph and on other roads of 40 mph, what is the quickest route?
   (iii) What speed would you need to average on the motorway to make it worth joining the M5 at an earlier junction than in (ii)?
   (iv) Roadworks are scheduled on the M5 between junctions 6 and 7, reducing the average speed over this section to 20 mph. Will this affect the route in (ii)?

(b) The managing director of the company lives in Tewkesbury. Using the speeds given in (a)(ii), what routes should he use to travel to the factories in
   (i)   Kidderminster
   (ii) Cheltenham?
   Will his best route to Kidderminster be affected by the forthcoming roadworks?

Decision and Discrete Mathematics

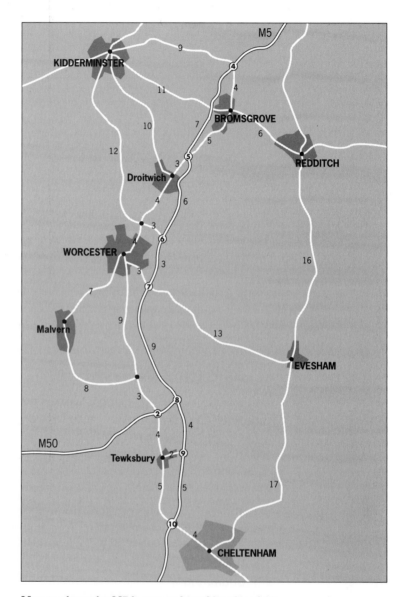

Map to show the M5 between junctions 4 and 10

Investigations

1. We have only applied Dijkstra's algorithm to a network diagram. Consider how you would adapt the algorithm if the network information were presented in the form of a distance table like this.

	Dorchester	Puddletown	Blandford	Wimborne	Bere Regis	Lytchett Minster	Weymouth	Warmwell	Wareham	Swanage	Poole
Dorchester	—	5	∞	∞	∞	∞	8	5	∞	∞	∞
Puddletown	5	—	12	∞	6	∞	∞	9	14	∞	∞
Blandford	∞	12	—	7	9	11	∞	∞	16	∞	∞
Wimborne	∞	∞	7	—	8	7	∞	∞	∞	∞	7
Bere Regis	∞	6	9	8	—	8	19	11	8	∞	∞
Lytchett Minster	∞	∞	11	7	8	—	25	∞	5	∞	6
Weymouth	8	∞	∞	∞	19	25	—	7	∞	∞	∞
Warmwell	5	9	∞	∞	11	∞	7	—	13	∞	∞
Wareham	∞	14	16	∞	8	5	∞	13	—	10	∞
Swanage	∞	∞	∞	∞	∞	∞	∞	∞	10	—	∞
Poole	∞	∞	∞	7	∞	6	∞	∞	∞	∞	—

∞ means no direct connection.

2. The following is an alternative algorithm, due to Ford, for finding the shortest distance between two nodes of a network. Investigate how it works and compare it with Dijkstra's algorithm.

Step 1   Let X_0 be the departure node. Put the value 0 against X_0 and values of ∞ against the other nodes.

Step 2   Apply the following rule: if λ_i is the value against X_i, look for an arc (X_i, X_j) such that
$\lambda_j - \lambda_i > d(X_i, X_j)$
where $d(X_i, X_j)$ is the length of arc (X_i, X_j). Replace λ_j by $\lambda_i + d(X_i, X_j)$.
Continue until there is no arc which will lead to a decrease in any λ_j. The resulting values of λ_j will then be the shortest distances from X_0 to each node X_j.

Step 3   The shortest path can then be found by the same procedure as in the Dijkstra algorithm.

3. Solve the pair of problems below and consider how you could adapt Dijkstra's algorithm to solve such problems in general. Note that in

Investigations continued

these networks the nodes are clearly marked and that arcs do not meet at the other crossings. These would be places where the roads went over or under each other.

(a) **Weight restriction problem**

The numbers on the arcs in the network below are the maximum weights in tons that those arcs can withstand (because of bridges with weight restrictions and so on). What is the heaviest vehicle that can be driven from S to T?

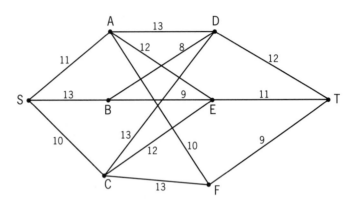

(b) **Freight aircraft problem**

A freight aircraft wishes to fly from S to T. In order to maximise its cargo load it needs to keep the fuel carried to a minimum. This means that short hops are preferable to a long haul. You require the route for which the longest hop is as small as possible. What route should you choose?

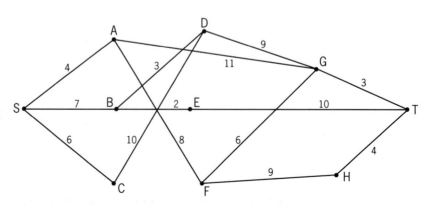

Note: distances are in hundreds of miles

4. (a) A haulage contractor has a lorry at town S. She needs to get it to town T at minimum cost. The network below represents the roads connecting S and T. The numbers alongside each edge give the costs in £s of sending the lorry along that road. In one case the cost in one direction along a road is positive, but in the other is negative, representing profit, because the lorry may collect and deliver a number of parcels *en route*, if the contractor so wishes.

JMB

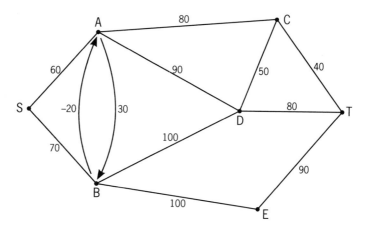

(b) Explain why Dijkstra's algorithm fails in this example and suggest how this problem might be overcome. Test your ideas on the following problem, in which the aim is again to travel from S to T at the minimum cost.

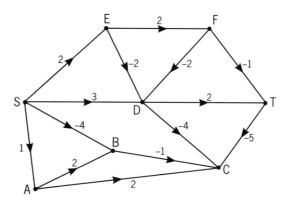

5. Adapt Dijkstra's algorithm to find the *longest* path through a network and apply the amended algorithm to Exercise 3B, 1a, b and c.

Investigations continued

6. The diagram below is a map of a small section of the London Underground. Investigate the quickest route between pairs of named stations. Assume that the time to travel one section (between neighbouring stations) is 2 minutes and that transfer between lines including waiting time takes 6 minutes.

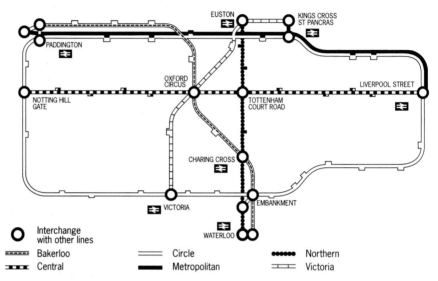

7. Write computer programs for Dijkstra's and Ford's algorithms.

KEY POINTS

When you have read this chapter you should

- know that Dijkstra's Algorithm is a way of finding the shortest route between two nodes of a network;
- understand the limitations of Dijkstra's Algorithm;
- recognise problems to which Dijkstra's Algorithm might usefully be applied.

4

Minimum Connector Problem

A cable TV company based in Plymouth wishes to make connections in the most economical way to all the towns in the South West shown on the map. They must therefore link all towns using as little cable as possible.

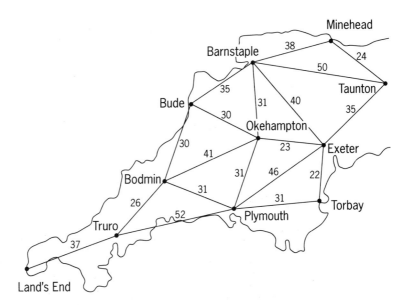

Try to solve this problem before you read any further. Later on you can compare the strategy you used with the algorithms given in the chapter.

Consider the network in figure 4.1(a) overleaf with its arcs removed (as in figure 4.1(b)). The minimum connector problem is to make a selection of the available arcs so that any one node can be reached from any other, and such that the total length of the chosen arcs is as small as possible. Clearly the resulting choice will contain no loops: if A, B and F are linked as shown in figure 4.2, B is already connected to F via A so it is unnecessary to choose arc BF.

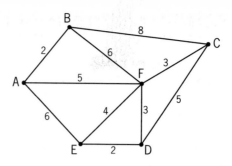

Figure 4.1(a)

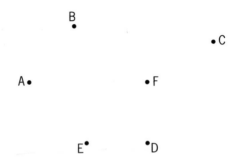

Figure 4.1(b)

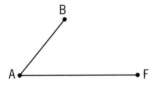

Figure 4.2

A set of arcs with no loops is called a tree, and the set which solves the minimum connector problem is referred to as the minimal spanning tree for the network. The problem of identifying the minimal spanning tree is a real one for cable TV companies, since provided each town is connected in some way to the base station it will still receive the signal. Thus the only concern of the company is to keep the total length of cable required to a minimum. For this reason, the problem is often called the Cable TV Problem.

Minimal Spanning Tree Algorithms

We shall consider two similar algorithms that can be used to solve the Cable TV Problem. Both are examples of 'greedy algorithms': ones that maximise immediate rewards regardless of future consequences. Although such methods do not usually lead to optimal solutions, the minimum connector algorithms are an exception, and both of the algorithms that follow produce optimal solutions. However, one of them is more amenable to computer solution than the other.

Kruskal's Algorithm

First select the shortest arc of the network.
At each subsequent stage, select from those arcs that have not yet been selected the shortest arc that does not link nodes between which a route has already been created. For a network with n nodes, when $n - 1$ arcs have been selected a minimal spanning tree will have been found.
If at any stage there is a choice of shortest arcs, choose arbitrarily between them.

Let us look at the stages involved in applying the algorithm to the network in figure 4.3.

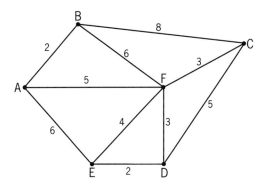

Figure 4.3

Arcs ranked in order of increasing length.

Length	Arcs
2	AB, DE
3	CF, DF
4	EF
5	CD, AF
6	AE
8	BC

1. We can start by selecting AB or DE, so let us arbitrarily select AB as shown in figure 4.4.

Figure 4.4

2. Select DE as is figure 4.5.

Figure 4.5

3. We can select CF or DF, so let us arbitrarily select DF as in figure 4.6.

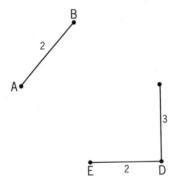

Figure 4.6

4. Select CF (figure 4.7).

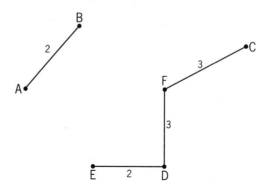

Figure 4.7

5. The next shortest arc is EF but E and F are already connected via D, so we do not select EF.

6. The next shortest arcs are CD and AF but C and D are already connected via F, so we choose AF (figure 4.8).

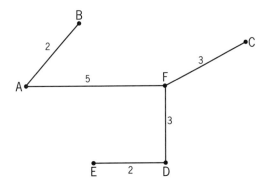

Figure 4.8

We have now selected five arcs and so all six nodes are connected. The minimal spanning tree has a length of 15.

Prim's Algorithm

First select an arbitrary node, then connect it to the nearest node.
Now connect the nearest node that is not already connected, to those already in the solution.
Repeat this until all nodes have been connected.
Here is Prim's algorithm applied to the network we used to demonstrate Kruskal's algorithm.

1. Select an arbitrary node, F say. Connect it to the nearest node: C and D are both distance 3 away, so arbitrarily choose C as in figure 4.9.

Figure 4.9

2. D is the nearest node not yet in the solution so we connect this next (figure 4.10).

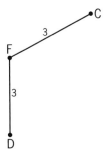

Figure 4.10

3. E is now the nearest node not yet in the solution so this is connected next (figure 4.11).

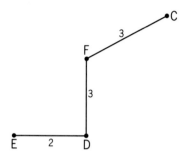

Figure 4.11

4. A is now the nearest node not yet in the solution so this is now connected (figure 4.12).

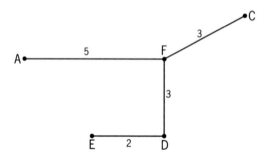

Figure 4.12

5. Finally connect B. Notice that this gives the same minimal spanning tree as before, of length 15 (figure 4.13).

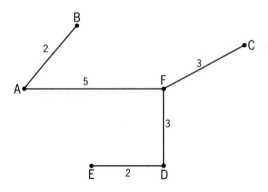

Figure 4.13

Exercise 4A

Find the minimal spanning tree and associated shortest distances for each of the networks below.

1.

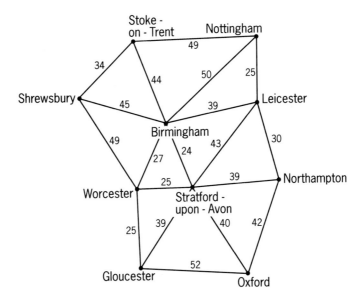

2.

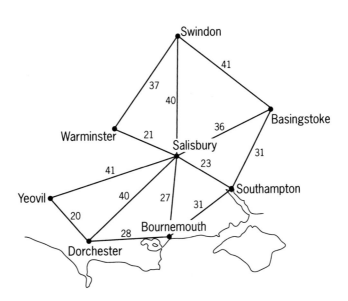

3.

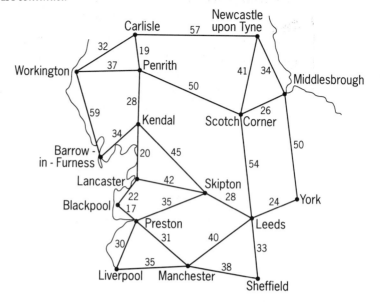

4.

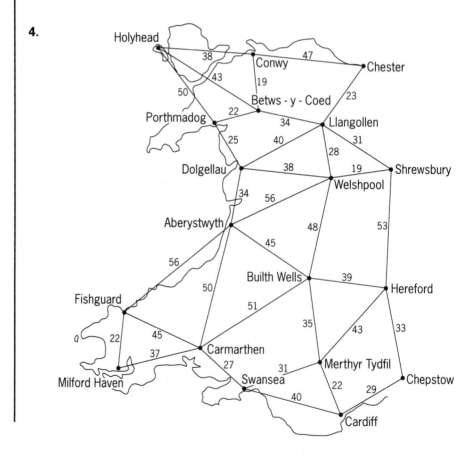

Now that you have had the opportunity to apply the algorithms to some networks, you can consider how to apply them when the network is given in the form of a distance table. This would be the form in which we would need to supply the network details to a computer, so in this form the algorithms could be automated.

Kruskal's algorithm is not particularly well suited to computer implementation as it requires the arcs to be arranged in order of length. This would mean using one of the sorting algorithms from Chapter 2. It also needs a way of recognising when cycles might be created, which is particularly tricky on a computer. You might like to consider why it is difficult to write such an algorithm by having a go at writing one yourself.

Prim's algorithm, on the other hand, is far more suitable for computerisation so we shall look at its application in tabular form in detail. We shall take the example we looked at earlier and show alongside the tables the corresponding steps from the diagrammatic approach. The distance table is shown below.

	A	B	C	D	E	F
A	—	2	∞	∞	6	5
B	2	—	8	∞	∞	6
C	∞	8	—	5	∞	3
D	∞	∞	5	—	2	3
E	6	∞	∞	2	—	4
F	5	6	3	3	4	—

(∞ indicates no direct link)

1. Select an arbitrary node, say F, and delete its row. (This is equivalent to ignoring nodes that are already connected in the network method). Look for the smallest entry in the column for the selected node, in this case F. There are two 3s so arbitrarily choose the one in row C. Add the new node, in this case node C, to the solution with arc CF. This is shown in figure 4.14.

Figure 4.14

	A	B	C	D	E	F
A	—	2	∞	∞	6	5
B	2	—	8	∞	∞	6
C	∞	8	—	5	∞	3
D	∞	∞	5	—	2	3
E	6	∞	∞	2	—	4

2. Delete row C and look for the smallest entry in columns F and C (figure 4.15).

The 3 in column F, row D is the smallest so we add node D to the solution with arc DF.

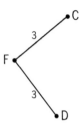

Figure 4.15

	A	B	C	D	E	F
A	–	2	∞	∞	6	5
B	2	–	8	∞	∞	6
D	∞	∞	5	–	2	3
E	6	∞	∞	2	–	4

3. Delete row D and look for the smallest entry in columns F, C and D. The 2 in column D, row E is the smallest so we add node E to the solution with arc ED (figure 4.16).

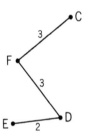

Figure 4.16

	A	B	C	D	E	F
A	–	2	∞	∞	6	5
B	2	–	8	∞	∞	6
E	6	∞	∞	2	–	4

4. Delete row E and look for the smallest entry in columns F, C, D and E.

The 5 in column F, row A is the smallest, so we add node A to the solution with arc FA (figure 4.17).

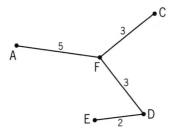

Figure 4.17

	A	B	C	D	E	F
A	–	2	∞	∞	6	5
B	2	–	8	∞	∞	6

5. Finally delete row A and look for the smallest entry in columns F, C, D, E and A. At this stage B is the only row left, because B is the only node not connected.

The smallest entry is the 2 in column A, row B so we add node B to the solution with arc AB (see figure 4.18).

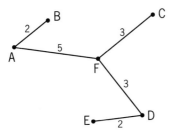

Figure 4.18

	A	B	C	D	E	F
B	2	–	8	∞	∞	6

In practice you would not have to rewrite the table at each stage but simply cross out the rows of the original table, and progressively tick the columns from which you can select.

Exercise 4B

1. Find the minimal spanning tree for the following networks which is given in tabular form.

	Malvern	Worcester	Hereford	Evesham	Ross	Tewkesbury	Gloucester	Cheltenham
Malvern	—	8	19	∞	19	13	20	∞
Worcester	8	—	25	16	∞	15	∞	∞
Hereford	19	25	—	∞	14	∞	28	∞
Evesham	∞	16	∞	—	∞	13	∞	16
Ross	19	∞	14	∞	—	24	16	∞
Tewkesbury	13	15	∞	13	24	—	10	9
Gloucester	20	∞	28	∞	16	10	—	9
Cheltenham	∞	∞	∞	16	∞	9	9	—

2. Find the minimal spanning tree for this network.

	Dorchester	Puddletown	Blandford	Wimborne	Bere Regis	Lytchett Minster	Weymouth	Warmwell	Wareham	Swanage	Poole
Dorchester	—	5	∞	∞	∞	∞	8	5	∞	∞	∞
Puddletown	5	—	12	∞	6	∞	∞	9	14	∞	∞
Blandford	∞	12	—	7	9	11	∞	∞	16	∞	∞
Wimborne	∞	∞	7	—	8	7	∞	∞	∞	∞	7
Bere Regis	∞	6	9	8	—	8	19	11	8	∞	∞
Lytchett Minster	∞	∞	11	7	8	—	25	∞	5	∞	6
Weymouth	8	∞	∞	∞	19	25	—	7	∞	∞	∞
Warmwell	5	9	∞	∞	11	∞	7	—	13	∞	∞
Wareham	∞	14	16	∞	8	5	∞	13	—	10	∞
Swanage	∞	∞	∞	∞	∞	∞	∞	∞	10	—	∞
Poole	∞	∞	∞	7	∞	6	∞	∞	∞	∞	—

Investigations

Problems 1 and 2 introduce situations in which there are only nodes, no established arcs. This gives you a free choice in selecting arcs. To produce a minimal spanning tree we would draw arcs from node to node, and would not create any new nodes, but you might like to consider whether a relaxation of this requirement would lead to a better solution to these two problems.

1. The diagram below shows a set of points on a printed circuit board which need to be joined together as economically as possible (i.e. using the shortest possible length of conductor), so that they can all be supplied with power. How should this be done?

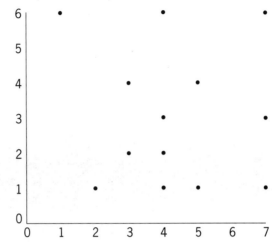

2. The UKG gas company has six sites in the North Sea. The locations are shown on the following map. Pipelines are to be laid to take the oil from the fields to Aberdoon on shore. Advise on the most economic way to achieve this.

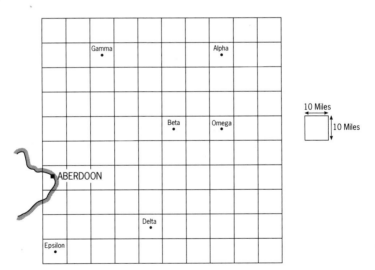

3. In practice, networks are not usually as simple as the diagrams we have been working on would suggest, and some preparatory work must be done to extract the information relevant to the problem in hand. Simplify the map overleaf and hence find the minimum rail network that will still allow rail connections between the towns shown.

Investigations continued

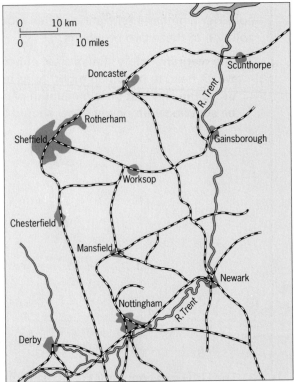

4. A cable TV company based in Hull wishes to connect the towns shown in the map below. They wish to know whether or not it is worth approaching the owners of the Humber Bridge with a view to running cables over the bridge. Minimum inter-town distances, with and without making use of the bridge, are given below in kilometres. Investigate the saving in cable that would result from using the bridge.

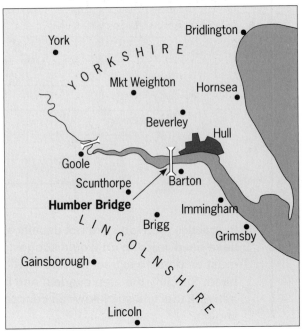

Table 1: Without using bridge.

	1	2	3	4	5	6	7	8	9	10	11	12	13	14
1 Hull		12	60	51	90	77	97	35	126	93	121	119	31	42
2 Beverley			47	32	87	74	103	23	122	90	122	116	18	39
3 York				64	87	74	103	69	122	90	122	116	29	39
4 Bridlington					119	106	135	26	154	122	154	148	48	71
5 Brigg						12	16	103	39	31	35	29	56	48
6 Scunthorpe							29	109	48	27	48	42	58	35
7 Barton								122	35	47	32	26	87	64
8 Hornsea									149	113	142	138	40	61
9 Lincoln										29	55	55	106	84
10 Gainsborough											56	56	74	51
11 Grimsby												16	106	84
12 Immingham													100	77
13 Mkt. Weighton														23
14 Goole														

Table 2: Using the bridge.

	1	2	3	4	5	6	7	8	9	10	11	12	13	14
1 Hull		12	60	51	26	42	13	35	69	56	53	45	31	42
2 Beverley			47	32	64	55	26	23	74	69	66	58	18	39
3 York				64	73	74	73	69	122	87	113	105	18	39
4 Bridlington					73	93	64	26	113	108	105	97	48	71
5 Brigg						12	16	87	39	31	35	29	39	48
6 Scunthorpe							29	77	48	27	48	42	58	35
7 Barton								48	55	47	32	26	43	39
8 Hornsea									97	92	89	80	40	61
9 Lincoln										29	55	55	98	84
10 Gainsborough											56	56	74	51
11 Grimsby												16	84	68
12 Immingham													77	61
13 Mkt. Weighton														23
14 Goole														

5. Write a computer program to apply Prim's algorithm to a network presented in tabular form.

6. (a) Four new villages are to built at the corners of a square of side 10 km. The local authority is very short of money and wishes to design a road system to link them together as economically as possible.
The first plan that was presented to them was simply a square of four roads with a total distance of 40 km. The treasurer said this was out of the question. 'We can't even afford 30 km' he told the Planning Committee. Can you help?

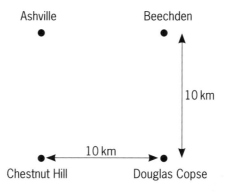

Investigations continued

(b) The inhabitants of the planet Morg live underground. They are excavating a new structure consisting of eight spherical chambers at the corners of a cube of side 1 km. They wish to link the chambers by tunnels. What is the most economic way to achieve this, assuming that tunnelling is equally expensive in all directions?

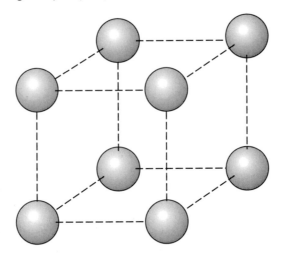

KEY POINTS

When you have read this chapter you should

- know that the minimum connector problem is that of linking all the nodes of a network using just those arcs which give the minimum total distance;
- know that the chosen arcs form what is called a Minimal Spanning Tree;
- be able to use Prim's Algorithm for a problem presented as a network or a table;
- be able to use Kruskal's Algorithm for a problem presented as a network.

5 The Travelling Salesman Problem

The advertisement below shows the sequence of venues in a White Light concert tour. With concerts almost every day and a lot of travelling in between, this will have been a tiring schedule. Assuming that the concert halls were free, could the sequence of towns and cities be arranged in a better way to cut down on the total distance travelled?

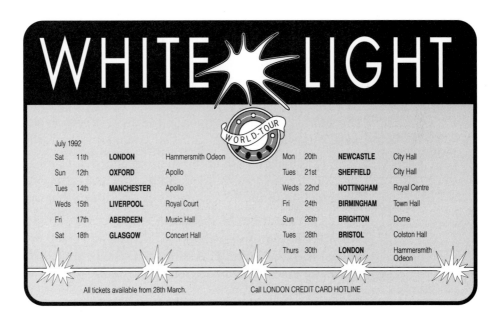

WHITE ★ LIGHT

WORLD-TOUR

July 1992

Sat	11th	**LONDON**	Hammersmith Odeon		Mon	20th	**NEWCASTLE**	City Hall
Sun	12th	**OXFORD**	Apollo		Tues	21st	**SHEFFIELD**	City Hall
Tues	14th	**MANCHESTER**	Apollo		Weds	22nd	**NOTTINGHAM**	Royal Centre
Weds	15th	**LIVERPOOL**	Royal Court		Fri	24th	**BIRMINGHAM**	Town Hall
Fri	17th	**ABERDEEN**	Music Hall		Sun	26th	**BRIGHTON**	Dome
Sat	18th	**GLASGOW**	Concert Hall		Tues	28th	**BRISTOL**	Colston Hall
					Thurs	30th	**LONDON**	Hammersmith Odeon

All tickets available from 28th March.   Call LONDON CREDIT CARD HOTLINE

Problems like those of the concert tour are called *travelling salesman problems* after the classic situation of a sales representative who has to make a round trip, starting at his home town, visiting a sequence of other towns and finally returning home. The problem is to choose a route that minimises the total distance travelled.

In order to get a feel for the problem, try the following exercise before reading any further.

Exercise 5A

A bread delivery van delivers each day to the towns shown below. Find the route with the smallest distance which starts at the bakery in Worcester, passes through each town at least once and returns to Worcester.

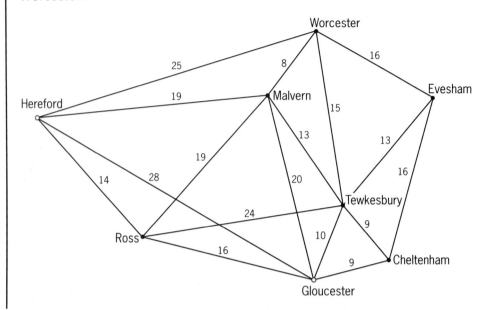

The shortest distance is given in the answer section at the back of the book. How close did you get? Did you adopt any particular strategy?

As in the shortest path and minimum connector problems the solution for a small network can be found by trial and error, but again we are concerned with the development of algorithms that can be applied in a systematic way to larger problems.

We will start our investigation by looking at a small problem with five towns, A, B, C, D and E. Assume A is the home town. The table below shows the distance from each town to all the others.

	A	B	C	D	E
A	–	8	10	11	7
B	8	–	17	5	14
C	10	17	–	12	9
D	11	5	12	–	11
E	7	14	9	11	–

As the salesman leaves his home town A, he has the choice of going to any one of the remaining four towns: assume he goes to C. From town C he can travel to any one of the remaining three – B, D or E, of which he chooses E. Suppose his next choice is B, then he must choose D and finally return to A. This is shown in figure 5.1.

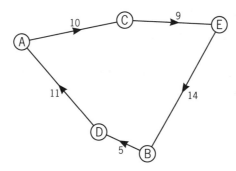

Figure 5.1

The ordering of the towns A–C–E–B–D–A is called a tour. The distance between two towns, say A and C, is denoted d_{AC}.
For our tour the total distance is

$$d_{AC} + d_{CE} + d_{EB} + d_{BD} + d_{DA} = 10 + 9 + 14 + 5 + 11$$
$$= 49$$

The five town problem would appear by inspection to have a total of $4 \times 3 \times 2 \times 1 = 24$ possible tours, but since the distance table is symmetric (i.e. $d_{XY} = d_{YX}$ for all pairs of towns X and Y), a tour such as A–D–B–E–C–A is equivalent to A–C–E–B–D–A. It has the same total distance. Thus the number of distinct tours is only 12.

For such a small problem we could easily examine all the possible tours. The minimum distance in this case turns out to be 41. However, for n towns it can be shown that there are $(n-1)!/2$ possible tours. To investigate all of these, even with a powerful computer capable of checking 1000 tours per second, soon becomes unreasonable. The table below illustrates the surprising amounts of time required.

Number of towns, n	$(n-1)!/2$	Computer time required to check all tours
10	181 440	3 mins.
12	2×10^7	≈ 5.5 hrs.
15	$\approx 4.4 \times 10^{10}$	≈ 1.4 yrs.
20	$\approx 6.1 \times 10^{16}$	≈ 2 million yrs

Clearly a method of solution based on an exhaustive evaluation of all tours is not practical. In fact, all the methods discovered to date that guarantee to find the optimum solution either take too long or need too much computer storage capacity (or both) as the size of the problem becomes larger.

Upper and Lower Bounds

Since it is difficult to find the optimum solution to larger problems, it is quite useful to be able to say that we know that the shortest tour lies between two distances. We call these the lower and upper bounds.

A lower bound, L, is a distance less than or equal to the shortest tour. An upper bound, U, is a distance greater than or equal to the shortest tour. Thus we can write

$$L \leqslant \text{shortest tour} \leqslant U$$

Ideally we want to find a lower bound as large as possible and an upper bound as small as possible, so that we narrow down the interval in which we know the shortest tour to lie. One method of finding bounds makes use of the minimum spanning trees that we met in the last chapter. To illustrate the technique, consider the following very trivial four town problem.

	A	B	C	D
A	—	3	7	6
B	3	—	2	5
C	7	2	—	6
D	6	5	6	—

The associated network is shown in figure 5.2.

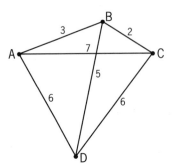

Figure 5.2

Using Prim's or Kruskal's algorithm we can obtain the minimum connector solution shown in figure 5.3, with a total distance of $3 + 2 + 5 = 10$.

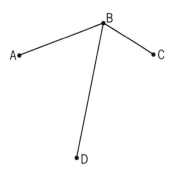

Figure 5.3

Clearly a possible, though highly inefficient, travelling salesman tour would be A–B–D–B–C–B–A, giving a total distance of 20. In this solution B is visited three times! In practice we would only consider visiting a town more than once if the nature of the network made this necessary. In general this tour would involve travelling along each arc of your minimum connector solution twice as shown in figure 5.4.

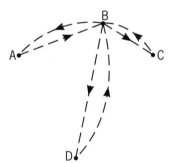

Figure 5.4

You can therefore see that doubling the solution of the minimum connector problem for the network gives us a crude upper bound. We can often make improvements to this tour by taking short-cuts, in this case we could go to C from D instead of retracing our path via B, to produce a tour of length 19 and hence a better upper bound. In a more complicated example you may be able to find several short-cuts to improve on this initial tour. Can you find another short-cut in this case?

By making a further short-cut to the above, or by inspection, we can find an upper bound of 17 with the tour A–B–C–D–A. The length of *any* tour we find actually gives us an upper bound, as the optimum solution is clearly no longer than this but may be shorter.

We now turn our attention to finding a lower bound, a value less than which we know the shortest tour cannot be. Again we make use of the minimum connector problem.

1. Remove one of the towns from the network, say A.

2. Solve the minimum connector problem for this reduced network, as in figure 5.5.

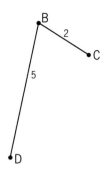

Figure 5.5

Distance = 7

3. Now link in A using the two shortest arcs, in this case AB and AD (figure 5.6).

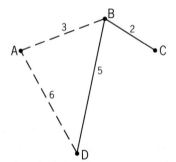

Figure 5.6

Distance = 7 + 3 + 6
       = 16

The result is not a tour, as we would need to travel along BC twice to give a tour of length 18. However it does give a lower bound for all tours, because B, C and D have been linked optimally and A has been added using the shortest possible arcs. If after this procedure we do end up with a tour, then it will be optimal, and this will happen with certain networks. Otherwise the distance gives a lower bound to all tours.

Other lower bounds can be found by repeating the procedure with a different town removed each time. In this way we can find five lower bounds, and the best of these will be the largest.

Removing B first gives a total distance of 12, as in figure 5.7.

Linking B using the shortest arcs then gives a distance of
12 + 3 + 2 = 17, as in figure 5.8.

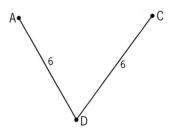

Figure 5.7

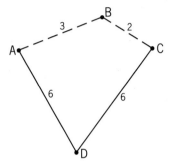

Figure 5.8

This is a tour so it must be the optimal solution, since A, D and C are joined optimally and B has been linked in optimally. There is no point continuing to find the other lower bounds by removing C and D. It is unfortunately rather unusual for this to happen in a larger problem, since it requires that when the omitted node is joined to the minimal spanning tree of the other nodes, a tour is produced.

If we had been content with our first attempts at upper and lower bounds we would have concluded that

$$16 \leqslant \text{shortest tour} \leqslant 20$$

but further investigation led us to reduce our upper bound to 17 and to raise our lower bound to 17. So we have

$$17 \leqslant \text{shortest tour} \leqslant 17$$

$$\text{i.e. shortest tour} = 17$$

Usually, further investigation will lead to a narrowing of the gap between lower and upper bounds. It is rare that we can close it in this way.

If the network were given in the form of a table we could use Prim's algorithm to solve the minimum connector problems, and thus to identify lower and upper bounds by computer.

Decision and Discrete Mathematics

Exercise 5B

1. Find upper and lower bounds for the five town problem given earlier. Here is the distance table again.

	A	B	C	D	E
A	–	8	10	11	7
B	8	–	17	5	14
C	10	17	–	12	9
D	11	5	12	–	11
E	7	14	9	11	–

2. Find upper and lower bounds for the bread delivery problem at the beginning of the chapter.

3. Investigate bounds for the following problem. A traveller from London plans to visit five towns on one of her business trips and wishes to minimise the length of her journey. The places she has to visit are Chester, Dover, Glasgow, Oxford and Plymouth. The inter-town distances are given in the table below.

	London	Chester	Dover	Glasgow	Oxford	Plymouth
London	–	182	70	399	56	214
Chester	182	–	255	229	132	267
Dover	70	255	–	472	127	287
Glasgow	399	229	472	–	356	484
Oxford	56	132	127	356	–	179
Plymouth	214	267	287	484	179	–

Heuristic Algorithms

We first met heuristic algorithms in Chapter 1 in the Bin Packing Problem. Heuristic algorithms for the travelling salesman problem can usually be divided into three parts:
(i)   a starting point;
(ii) a solution improvement scheme;
(iii) a termination rule.
The tour achieved at termination generally depends on the starting point.

The algorithms fall into two main categories, *tour building* algorithms and *tour to tour improvement* algorithms.

Tour Building

The starting point for a tour building algorithm is an arbitrary town. From this town we successively include other towns until a tour is achieved. A very simple scheme of this type is the *nearest neighbour rule* (another example of a greedy algorithm).

Step 1   Select any town as the starting point.

Step 2   From the towns not already in the sequence, find the town nearest to the last town selected. Add it to the sequence. Make an arbitrary choice in the event of a tie.

Step 3   Repeat Step 2 until all towns are included in the sequence, then join the first and last towns to form a tour.

The resulting tour depends on the town chosen to start the sequence.

We shall apply this scheme to the bakery problem shown again in figure 5.9.

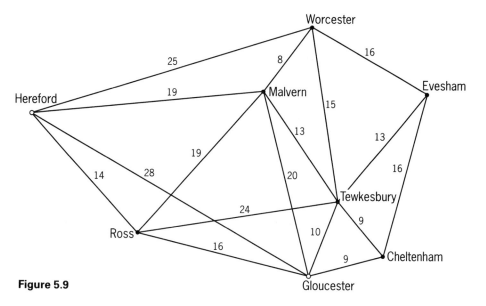

Figure 5.9

Starting at Worcester the nearest town is

Malvern		8
→	Tewkesbury	8 + 13 = 21
→	Cheltenham	21 + 9 = 30
→	Gloucester	30 + 9 = 39
→	Ross	39 + 16 = 55
→	Hereford	55 + 14 = 69

At this point we meet a problem, because the only remaining place to visit is Evesham and there is no direct link. We find the shortest route from Hereford to Evesham by inspection or by applying Dijkstra's algorithm. This is 41 via Worcester, so continuing,

→	Evesham	69 + 41 = 110

and finally returning to Worcester,

$\quad\quad\quad\quad\rightarrow\quad$ Worcester $\quad\quad\quad\quad\quad\quad\quad\quad\quad\quad 110 + 16 = 126$

Alternatively, starting at Evesham, we proceed as follows.

$\rightarrow$	Tewkesbury	13
$\rightarrow$	Cheltenham	$13 + \ 9 = 22$
$\rightarrow$	Gloucester	$22 + \ 9 = 31$
$\rightarrow$	Ross	$31 + 16 = 47$
$\rightarrow$	Hereford	$47 + 14 = 61$
$\rightarrow$	Malvern	$61 + 19 = 80$
$\rightarrow$	Worcester	$80 + \ 8 = 88$
$\rightarrow$	Evesham	$88 + 16 = 104$

Try some other starting points for yourself.

Tour to Tour Improvement

The starting point for a tour to tour improvement algorithm is an arbitrary tour. The solution generation scheme is a rule for finding a shorter tour by making a modification to the present tour (for example by interchanging the order in which two towns are visited). The procedure terminates when application of the rule for finding a shorter tour yields no further improvement.

Tour to tour improvement methods tend to be rather tedious for manual computation since the rule for finding a shorter tour may have to be applied many times. Any change in order is as likely to increase as to decrease the tour distance, so much effort is employed in rejecting unprofitable amendments. The methods can, however, easily be programmed for computer solution and in this form can prove highly efficient. The final tour is dependent on the tour chosen as the starting point.

Two possible generation schemes are suggested below.

Scheme 1
Exchange arcs that connect towns in the tour with other arcs not in the tour whose distance is less than the arcs removed.
e.g. Suppose the present tour is A–B–C–D–E–A (see figure 5.10).

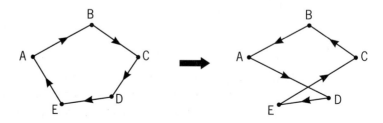

Figure 5.10

Consider removing two arcs that do not have a town in common, such as E–A and C–D.

If

$$d_{AD} + d_{EC} - (d_{EA} + d_{CD}) < 0$$

connect A–D and E–C. The new tour is A–D–E–C–B–A.

Scheme 2

This consists essentially of interchanging pairs of towns in the current tour. The first town in the sequence remains fixed throughout. We consider the possible improvement brought about by swapping the town in the second position with the town in each subsequent position, then make the most advantageous interchange. The process is repeated until no improvement can be made by swapping the town in the second position.

We now try swapping the town in the third position with towns in subsequent positions, again opting for the most advantageous change. This is repeated until no further improvement can be made. We then move on to the fourth position and so on until we reach the $(n-1)$th position (where n is the number of towns).

We complete this section by applying these two algorithms to the following problem.

	London	Liverpool	Manchester	Leeds	Cambridge	Birmingham	Cardiff	Preston	Nottingham
London	—	210	197	196	60	118	155	218	128
Liverpool		—	34	72	195	98	200	29	99
Manchester			—	43	153	88	188	32	71
Leeds				—	143	115	236	69	73
Cambridge					—	101	191	197	82
Birmingham						—	107	191	59
Cardiff							—	209	170
Preston								—	123
Nottingham									—

As stated earlier the tour to tour improvement methods are particularly tedious to apply manually, and computer programs are available to assist in their investigation. The solutions given to this problem are printouts from computer programs. Figures 5.11 and 5.12 show the result of using the tour to tour improvement algorithm, and figure 5.13 shows the result of using the nearest neighbour tour building algorithm.

```
    TRAVELLING SALESMAN-Tour to tour Scheme 1.
    File name: ?Example

    A London        B Liverpool
    C Manchester    D Leeds
    E Cambridge     F Birmingham
    G Cardiff       H Preston
    I Nottingham

    Initial route: ?ABCDEFGHIA

    Distance by this route is 1098

    Remove arcs:      A-B    and    E-F

    Reconnect with: A-E    and    B-F

    with a saving of   153

    New route is: A-E-D-C-B-F-G-H-I-A
    Distance by this route is 945

    Remove arcs:      E-D    and    G-H

    Reconnect with: E-G    and    D-H

    with a saving of  92

    New route is: A-E-G-F-B-C-D-H-I-A
    Distance by this route is 853

    Remove arcs:      E-G    and    I-A

    Reconnect with: E-I    and    G-A

    with a saving of  82

    New route is: A-E-I-H-D-C-B-F-G-A
    Distance by this route is 771

    Remove arcs:      I-H    and    D-C

    Reconnect with: I-D    and    H-C

    with a saving of  61

    New route is: A-E-I-D-H-C-B-F-G-A
    Distance by this route is 710

    Remove arcs:      D-H    and    C-B

    Reconnect with: D-C    and    H-B

    with a saving of  31

    New route is: A-E-I-D-C-H-B-F-G-A
    Distance by this route is 679

    SHORTEST ROUTE FOUND
    A E I D C H B F G A
    with distance 679
```

Figure 5.11

```
TRAVELLING SALESMAN-Tour to Tour improvement - Scheme 2

File name: ?Example

A London          B Liverpool
C Manchester      D Leeds
E Cambridge       F Birmingham
G Cardiff         H Preston
I Nottingham

Initial route: ?ABCDEFGHIA

Distance by this route is 1098

Interchange town in position: 2 ( B )

        with town in position: 5 ( E )

New route is: AECDBFGHIA
with distance 993

Interchange town in position: 2 ( E )

        with town in position: 8 ( H )

New route is: AHCDBFGEIA
with distance 971

Interchange town in position: 2 ( H )

        with town in position: 4 ( D )

New route is: ADCHBFGEIA
with distance 906

Interchange town in position: 7 ( G )

        with town in position: 9 ( I )

New route is: ADCHBFIEGA
with distance 885

Interchange town in position: 2 ( D )

        with town in position: 6 ( F )

New route is: AFCHBDIEGA
with distance 840

Interchange town in position: 2 ( F )

        with town in position: 8 ( E )

New route is: AECHBDIFGA
with distance 740

Interchange town in position: 3 ( C )

        with town in position: 6 ( D )

New route is: AEDHBCIFGA
with distance 727
SHORTEST ROUTE FOUND
```

Figure 5.12

```
              TRAVELLING SALESMAN-Nearest Neighbour
                 File name:  ?Example
              A.London               B.Liverpool
              C.Manchester           D.Leeds
              E.Cambridge            F.Birmingham
              G.Cardiff              H.Preston
              I.Nottingham


                    Tour                    Distance
              A E I F C H B D G A             813
              B H C D I F E A G B             752
              C H B D I F E A G C             769
              D C H B F I E A G D             794
              E A F I C H B D G E             868
              F I C H B D E A G F             728
              G F I C H B D E A G             728
              H B C D I F E A G H             763
              I F C H B D E A G I             808


              Shortest route found:

                         F  Birmingham
                         I  Nottingham
                         C  Manchester
                         H  Preston
                         B  Liverpool
                         D  Leeds
                         E  Cambridge
                         A  London
                         G  Cardiff
                         F  Birmingham
              with distance 728
```

Figure 5.13

The optimal solution is 679 miles, which is actually achieved by the tour to tour improvement technique. However, we can draw no conclusions about the comparative performance of these algorithms from a single example. We would have to analyse their results over a very large number of varied problems before we could make any meaningful comments.

Exercise 5C

Use the techniques that you have learned in this chapter, together with the Travelling Salesman Computer Package if you have access to it, to tackle these problems.

1. A group of tourists staying in Weston wishes to visit all the places shown on the following map. Suggest a route that will minimise their total driving distance.

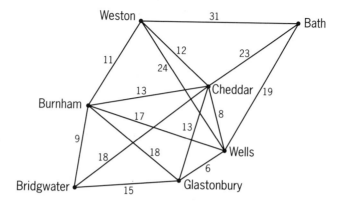

2. A depot located in Birmingham supplies goods to customers in Sheffield, Nottingham, Stoke, Shrewsbury, Hereford, Gloucester and Northampton. Plan a suitable route for the delivery lorry if it has to make deliveries in all of these towns on one trip.
The distances involved are shown in the table.

	Birmingham	Sheffield	Nottingham	Stoke	Shrewsbury	Hereford	Gloucester	Northampton
Birmingham	—	77	50	43	43	52	52	50
Sheffield	77	—	37	47	79	125	128	94
Nottingham	50	37	—	50	79	102	102	57
Stoke	43	47	50	—	34	83	89	85
Shrewsbury	43	79	79	34	—	52	75	93
Hereford	52	125	102	83	52	—	28	91
Gloucester	52	128	102	89	75	28	—	72
Northampton	50	94	57	85	93	91	72	—

3. The following problem appeared on the back of a packet of Quaker Oats some years ago. The problem is to calculate the shortest possible route, starting and finishing in St Hélier, visiting all the marked places. Although it is easy to find the answer by inspection, the problem is an interesting one to try with the algorithms. It would be a good idea to start by simplifying the network.

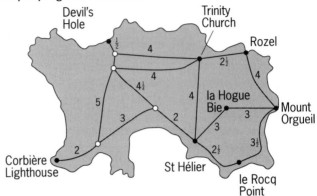

4. Apply some of the algorithms to the following famous travelling salesman problem known as *The Barachet Ten Town Problem*. The table of distances is given below.

	A	B	C	D	E	F	G	H	I	J
A	–	28	57	72	81	85	80	113	89	80
B		–	28	45	54	57	63	85	63	63
C			–	20	30	28	57	57	40	57
D				–	10	20	72	45	20	45
E					–	22	81	41	10	41
F						–	63	28	28	63
G							–	80	89	113
H								–	40	80
I									–	40
J										–

5. Find the shortest travelling salesman tour, starting and finishing at A, for the network below.

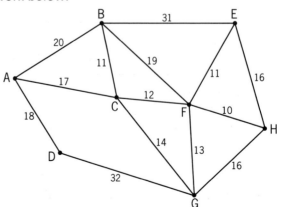

6. The map below shows six youth hostels, A, B, C, D, E and F, in an area of rough country, together with paths connecting them. The numbers by the paths show lengths in miles of sections of path.

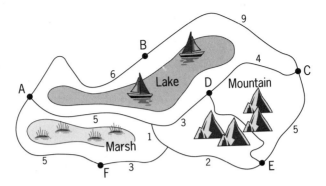

(a) Draw a network showing the shortest *direct* distances between youth hostels. For example, the shortest direct distance between E and F is 5 miles. However, between B and D there is no direct link. (You may do this by inspection. The application of an algorithm is not required.)

(b) Use Prim's algorithm to find a minimum spanning tree for your network. Describe each step in your use of the algorithm, and draw your minimum spanning tree.

(c) A walker wishes to spend a night at each hostel during her stay in the district, starting and ending at hostel A. Use your answer to part (b) to construct an upper bound for the distance which she must walk.

(d) If she requires to traverse the mountain pass between D and E, suggest how you might modify your use of Prim's algorithm in part (b) in order to construct an upper bound for the distance she must cover.

(OXFORD)

7. In a sweet-making factory, five flavours of fruit drop are made one after another on a single machine. After each flavour, the machine must be cleaned in readiness for the next flavour. The time spent cleaning depends on the two flavours as indicated in the table below.

Time in minutes	Next flavour to be made				
	Strawberry	**Lemon**	**Orange**	**Lime**	**Raspberry**
Last flavour made					
Strawberry	—	14	12	19	16
Lemon	21	—	14	10	19
Orange	19	16	—	17	20
Lime	17	9	13	—	15
Raspberry	20	15	13	19	—

The production manager wishes to find a sequence which minimises the total time spent cleaning the machine in each cycle from strawberry to strawberry, making each flavour of fruit drop once only per cycle.

(a) By constructing an appropriate network, explain how the problem may be formulated as a travelling salesman problem. Hence, by using the nearest unvisited city heuristic starting from strawberry, suggest a production sequence to the manager.

Someone notices that the smallest cleaning time is in changing from lime to lemon. Accordingly, he suggests that a better production sequence may be found by using the nearest unvisited city heuristic beginning from lime so that the sequence will begin with the change from lime to lemon.

(b) Determine whether he is right that a better sequence will be found.

(JMB)

Investigation

A depot located at town A supplies goods to customers in towns B, C, D and E. The inter-town distances are given in the table below.

	A	B	C	D	E
A	—	28	57	20	45
B	28	—	47	46	73
C	57	47	—	76	85
D	20	46	76	—	40
E	45	73	85	40	—

Usually a single vehicle will suffice for a particular delivery but today the customers' requirements are 100 units each and the vehicle available will only carry 300 units. Another similar vehicle can be hired locally, but how should the two vehicles be routed?

(Hint: introduce an artificial depot.)

KEY POINTS

When you have read this chapter you should

- understand that the Travelling Salesman Problem is that of finding the shortest route that will visit each node of a network (at least once) and return to the starting point;
- understand the definition of a *Tour*;
- know how to find upper and lower bounds for a solution;
- understand that exhaustive evaluation of all tours is not possible in more complex problems;
- understand that heuristic methods are required for more complex Travelling Salesman Problems, and if possible have experience of using
  (i) tour to tour improvement algorithms
  (ii) tour building algorithms.

6

The Route Inspection Problem

A heavy frost is forecast for the Isle of Wight and the local council in Newport has decided to send out its two gritting lorries to treat the main roads. One will treat the left hand and the other the right hand side of the roads. They will follow the same route in opposite directions. What route should they take?

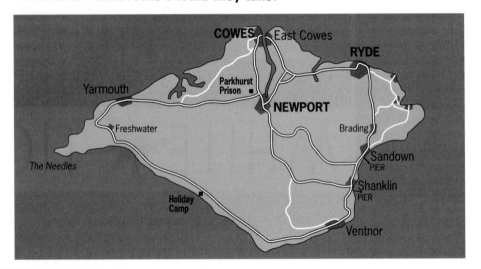

The problem faced here is to start from a node, travel along each arc and return to the starting point. If it is possible to achieve this without going over the same arc twice, the minimum distance is just the sum of the arc lengths. If it is necessary to cover some arcs twice, then we must select these in the most economic way. This type of problem is called a *Route Inspection Problem*. Before we consider how to approach route inspection problems, we need to look at some network theory.

Networks

Node type

An *n*-node is a node where *n* arcs join. Figure 6.1 shows a 3-node.

Figure 6.1

1-nodes, 3-nodes (and so on) are referred to as *odd* nodes;
2-nodes, 4-nodes (and so on) are referred to as *even* nodes.

Numbers of nodes

In any network there is always an even number of odd nodes. This can be proved as follows.

Adding together the node type numbers of all the nodes in a network will give twice the number of arcs. This is because each arc is counted twice, once from each end. Thus the sum of node type numbers is even for any network.

We can't have an odd number of odd nodes, because a sum containing an odd number of odd numbers would be odd. Thus any network must have an even number of odd nodes.

Traversability

A network is said to be *traversable* if you can draw it without removing your pen from the paper and without retracing the same arc twice.

Is the network shown in figure 6.2 traversable?

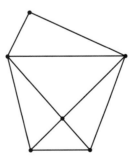

Figure 6.2

You have probably found that the network is traversable, but you must start at one odd node and end at the other (note that it has two odd nodes). If you investigate drawing other networks and note their node type numbers for each node, you will find that

for a network to be traversable it must have 0 or 2 odd nodes, and if we are to be able to start and finish at the same node it must have no odd nodes.

Application of Network Theory to Route Inspection Problems

The implications of this result about traversability for route inspection problems are as follows.

If there are no odd nodes in the network, the network is traversable. The minimum distance is the sum of the arc distances, so the problem is trivial.

Otherwise we know there will be an even number of odd nodes, and the route inspection algorithm requires that we identify them and link them together in pairs in the most economic way. The links selected will be repeated in the final route. The effect of adding these extra arcs is to make all nodes even and hence the network becomes traversible.

Now we are ready to try the following problem. A power station located at Z provides power for seven towns located at A, B, C, D, E, F and G. After some blizzards the engineer wants to go on a tour of inspection of the pylons and power lines. The lengths, in kilometres, are shown in figure 6.3. What is the shortest route the engineer can take for her inspection?

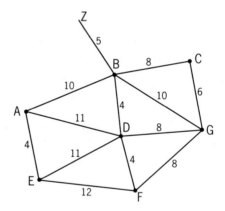

Figure 6.3

The odd nodes are Z, A, B, D, E and F as shown in figure 6.4.

Look at the distance between these nodes. If there is no direct link, we find the shortest route between each pair by inspection. In a more complex example, or on a computer, Dijkstra's algorithm could be used to find the shortest paths.

We must now pair up the six nodes in such a way as to give the smallest possible extra distance. This example is a simple one: it is fairly easy to see from the network diagram (without the help of the table) that the best pairing is ZB, AE and DF. In a more difficult example, a systematic analysis of the possibilities from the table could be undertaken.

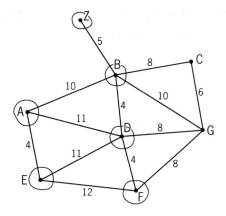

Figure 6.4

	Z	A	B	D	E	F
Z	—	15	5	9	19	13
A		—	10	11	4	15
B			—	4	14	8
D				—	11	4
E					—	12
F						—

The length of the shortest route is the sum of all the arc lengths plus the lengths of ZB, AE and DF.

Shortest route = 101 + 5 + 4 + 4
 = 114

One possible route of this length is shown in figure 6.5, but there are many.

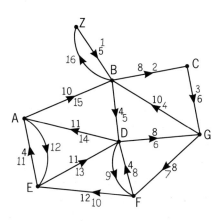

Figure 6.5

Exercise 6A

1. Solve the route inspection problem for the two networks given below.

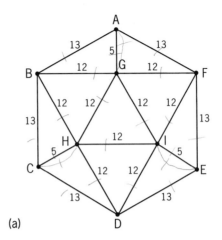

(a)

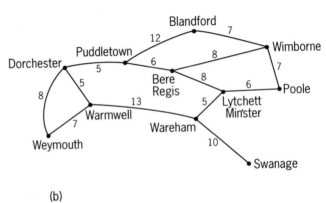

(b)

2. The airport plan below shows two runways R01 and R02 and taxi-ways to and from the apron in front of the terminal building.

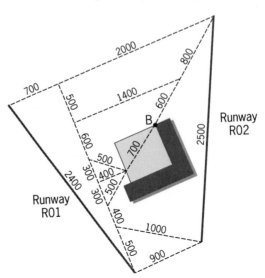

Each night when there are no flights, the runways and taxi-ways have to be inspected. The crew responsible for this job is based at B. What is the best route for this inspection

(a) if a single drive down each runway is sufficient?
(b) if the runways must be covered twice, once in each direction?

3. Solve the route inspection problem for the following network given in tabular form. Try to work without drawing the network, but if you are having difficulties you will find it in the chapter on the travelling salesman problem.

	Malvern	Worcester	Hereford	Evesham	Ross	Tewkesbury	Gloucester	Cheltenham
Malvern	—	8	19	∞	19	13	20	∞
Worcester	8	—	25	16	∞	15	∞	∞
Hereford	19	25	—	∞	14	∞	28	∞
Evesham	∞	16	∞	—	∞	13	∞	16
Ross	19	∞	14	∞	—	24	16	∞
Tewkesbury	13	15	∞	13	24	—	10	9
Gloucester	20	∞	28	∞	16	10	—	9
Cheltenham	∞	∞	∞	16	∞	9	9	—

4. A highways maintenance depot must inspect all the manhole covers within its area. The road network is given below. In order to do this an engineer must leave the depot, D, drive along each of the roads in the network at least once and return to the depot. What is the minimum distance that he must drive? Give a route which enables him to drive this distance.

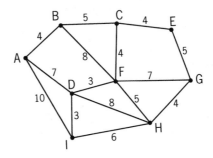

5. The island authorities of Elsea are based in St Oz and wish to inspect their road network for fallen trees after a night of strong gales. Advise on a suitable route, which should be as short as possible.

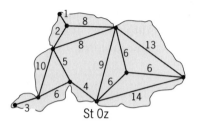

6. A policeman has to patrol the streets on the map below. Can you advise him on an efficient route?

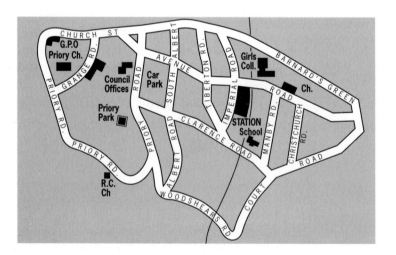

7. The following matrix gives fares for direct bus journeys between towns, P, Q, R, S, T, U and V, in a tourist area. Blanks indicate no direct service.

Fares in pence

	P	Q	R	S	T	U	V
P		57		35			70
Q	57		53	61		160	
R		53			49		
S	35	61			30		44
T			49	30		48	52
U		160			48		40
V	70			44	52	40	

(a) Draw a network to represent this information.

(b) Using Dijkstra's method, find the minimum cost route from P to U. Describe in full detail all of the steps of the method, specifying the order in which you assign values to vertices.

(c) A holidaymaker sets out from V to travel over all of the routes in the area, returning to V at the end. Find the minimum cost for the journey and the route that should be taken.
Explain the significance of towns P and U in your solution.

(d) A 'summertime special' service is to be provided linking R to S at a cost of 35p. What is the new minimum cost and the best route for the holidaymaker in part (c)? (In this part the necessary minimum connectors may be found by inspection.)

(OXFORD)

KEY POINTS

When you have read this chapter you should
- understand that the Route Inspection Problem is that of finding the shortest route to travel along each arc of a network (at least once) and return to the starting point;
- understand the term 'traversability' and be able to test whether a network is traversable;
- know how to use the algorithm to solve the problem.

7

Simulation

Suppose that a learner driver has a probability of $\frac{1}{3}$ of passing the driving test at any attempt, and that she takes the test until she passes. How may the process of taking the test be simulated by throwing a die? Would it be possible to use other equipment in the simulation instead of a die?

Suppose there are several such drivers. Simulate the process of each driver taking the test until he or she passes. Record the number of attempts needed for each driver to pass, and display your results in a suitable form. What is the mean number of attempts needed? What is the most likely number of attempts needed?

Monte Carlo Methods

The above situation could alternatively be analysed using probability theory. But many situations that we would like to analyse may well be too complicated even for sophisticated mathematical techniques. The investigation of the operation of queues is one such problem and we may need to answer questions such as the ones below.

- How should a set of traffic lights be set to give the best traffic flow?
- How should a doctor organise his surgery to minimise waiting times?
- What is the best queueing system for a bank or building society branch to operate to satisfy its customers?

It may be possible to investigate such questions by experimentation, for example you could try various settings of the traffic lights until you get the best result. However, this may take a long time and not be the most popular way! It is more likely that a simulation would be used. Simulation means the imitation of the operation of a system. You will probably have heard of flight simulators which are used in the training of aircraft pilots. This is one type of simulation – a *deterministic* simulation in which chance events do not occur. However, in this chapter we shall be looking at *stochastic* simulations. This means we shall be studying situations where chance affects the outcome. The methods we shall devise are commonly called *Monte Carlo methods*. Monte Carlo is famous for its casinos and for games of chance. Monte Carlo methods are so called because some kind of random device such as a die or coin or even a roulette wheel is used to imitate chance happenings in the real world.

Random devices

In the introductory problem you used a die to simulate the taking of a driving test. You probably devised a rule, such as 'if the die shows a 5 or 6 then the learner passes the test, if the die shows a 1, 2, 3 or 4 then she fails.'

You may prefer, instead, to use another random device such as the random number generator on your scientific calculator. On most calculators this is indicated by a symbol like $\boxed{\text{RAN\#}}$, and when pressed it will produce a random decimal fraction between 0 and 1. Pressing this key a few times on my calculator I obtain the following numbers.

0.611   0.539   0.068   0.468   0.084   0.304   0.175

I could therefore use the following rule to simulate the learner driver taking the driving test: 'If the random number generated is less than 0.333 then the learner driver passes the test; otherwise she fails.'

In fact this rule will give only a very good approximation to the correct probability of passing. Can you see why this is so? Can you suggest a rule to give precisely the correct probability?

Try some of the problems in Exercise 7A, either on your own or with a partner or group, before reading further. These will help you to see how to use simulations in different situations involving chance.

Exercise 7A

1. The Collector's Problem
A manufacturer of breakfast cereals is giving away cards with pictures of famous mathematicians on them. There are six different cards in the set, depicting the following mathematicians: Archimedes, Bolzano, Cardan, Descartes, Euler and Fermat.

Archimedes   Descartes   Euler

There is one card placed in each packet of cereal by the manufacturer. The different cards are distributed at random, and naturally I am keen to collect the set.

(a) Simulate, for example using a die, the number of packets I will need to buy to get at least one of each card. Perform the simulation several times, recording each time the number of packets that a collector buys before having a complete set.

(b) Display the data you obtain and find the mean number of cereal packets bought.

(c) How would you carry out the simulation if there were 10 cards in the set instead of six?

2. Pedestrian Crossings

The operation of a pedestrian crossing in a busy city centre can be modelled as follows.
Pedestrians wishing to cross the road from one side arrive at random, at an average rate of 1 every 10 seconds. We can model this by assuming that in any 5 second period there is a 0.5 probability of 0 pedestrians arriving and a 0.5 probability of 1 pedestrian arriving. (We assume, for the sake of simplicity, that no more than 1 pedestrian can arrive in the 5 second period.)

The first pedestrian to arrive at the crossing will press a button to request to cross. The lights then show 'Don't cross' for 25 seconds followed by 5 seconds of 'Cross'. During this 5 second period all the people waiting can cross.
(a) Use a coin to simulate the operation of the crossing for a period of about 300 seconds.

A table like the one below might help. Here, a tail (T) indicates no arrival, and a head (H) indicates one arrival in a given 5 second period. In the 'Lights' column, D = Don't cross, C = Cross.

Time	Result of random process	Size of queue	Lights
0	T	0	D
5	H	1	D
10	T	1	D
15	H	2	D
20	H	3	D
25	T	3	D
30	T	3	C
35	H	1	D

(b) Use the results of your simulation to display data showing
   (i) the number of people crossing each time;
   (ii) the total lengths of time for which the traffic is allowed to flow freely.

(c) There are some simple assumptions made in this model about how the pedestrians arrive and how the crossing operates once the button to cross is pushed. How might these be made more realistic?

3. If you have not yet done so, find and try out the random number generator on your scientific calculator. On most models a special key is provided, usually like this: $\boxed{\text{RAN\#}}$. Pressing the key will produce a random decimal fraction between 0 and 1.

   The BBC Basic statement

   PRINT RND (1)

   will produce the same on a BBC computer. Similar Basic statements exist on other types of computer.

   (a) How could you use a calculator or computer to simulate throwing a coin to get heads or tails?

   (b) Try the following if you have a computer or a graphics calculator available.

   On a computer (BBC Basic):   On a graphics calculator:

   ```
   10 X = RND (5)
   20 PRINT X
   30 GO TO 10
   ```

   $\boxed{\text{Int}}$ $\boxed{(}$ $\boxed{5}$ $\boxed{\times}$ $\boxed{\text{Ran \#}}$ $\boxed{)}$ $\boxed{\text{EXE}}$

   and keep pressing $\boxed{\text{EXE}}$

   Describe the output that is produced.

    (c) Modify the computer program or calculator instruction to:
      (i) simulate the throwing of a die;
      (ii) produce random digits in the range 0 to 9 (inclusive).

4. Repeat the driving test simulation from the beginning of the chapter several times, this time with a probability of success of 0.2 at each test. Work out the average number of attempts before a driver passes. Find, by experimentation, a connection between n, the average number of attempts to pass, and p, the probability of success at each attempt. If possible, compare your results with a theoretical analysis.

5. For the **Collector's Problem** (question 1) investigate how C, the average number of cards collected to get a complete set, varies with N, the number of cards in the set.

6. **Doctor's Surgery**

A doctor is analysing the amount of time that patients spend in her surgery waiting room. Her first appointment is at 9.00 a.m. and appointments are made at 10 minute intervals thereafter with the last appointment at 11.20 a.m. She observes that the time spent seeing each patient varies from 5 to 15 minutes. Her receptionist informs her that patients tend to arrive up to 5 minutes before their appointment times and are very rarely late.

Making suitable assumptions, which should be clearly stated, simulate the operation of the surgery for three separate mornings and find the patients' average waiting time. You may like to use a table like the one below.

Appointment	Random number	Arrival time	Consultation starts	Random number	Consultation finishes	Waiting time
9.00						
9.10						
9.20						
9.30						
9.40						
9.50						

Comment on your results.

7. **Random Walks**

Random walk is a term used in Physics for the movement of a particle in one, two or three dimensions, where at each stage the direction of the movement is affected by chance. Random walks are used to model the movement of molecules in gases and radioactive particles escaping through shielding. Using such methods it is possible to work out, for example, how thick the shielding on a nuclear fuel storage vessel needs to be to keep radioactivity outside it to a safe level.

In a simple random walk in one dimension we shall take two fixed points A and B 10 metres apart as in the figure below. A particle initially starts at 4 m from A and in every second it has a probability of ½ of moving one metre towards A and a probability of ½ of moving one metre towards B. The particle stops when it reaches A or B.

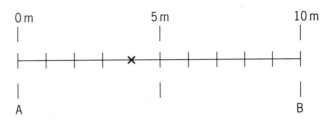

(a) Simulate this random walk several times and hence estimate
  (i) the probability of the particle reaching A;
  (ii) the average time that the particle takes to reach A or B.

(b) Try different starting positions.

Investigations

You can tackle most of these investigations by hand. Alternatively, you may prefer to use a short program on a programmable scientific calculator or computer.

1. Use the ideas developed in Exercise 7A to simulate the operation of a real pedestrian crossing or doctor's surgery or any other similar situation. You should start by studying the situation carefully and collecting any necessary data.

   A spreadsheet package could be used to help with a doctor's surgery investigation like the one in question 6 above.

2. Investigate further random walks in one dimension. Suppose for example that particles are emitted from the midpoint of AB. Find the average time the random walk lasts and investigate for different distances between A and B.

3. Investigate random walks in two dimensions. For example, in any second the particle might have an equal probability of moving one metre North, South, East or West. Find how the average distance of the object from its starting point varies with the number of steps.

4. It is often said that if enough monkeys sit at enough typewriters hitting the keys at random, then they will eventually produce the complete works of Shakespeare! Investigate the validity of this statement by using a computer program to simulate one monkey sitting at one computer. For example, how long will it take, on average, for one line of Shakespeare such as '*Now is the winter of our discontent*' to be produced?

5. Suppose that in a game of tennis the server has a probability of 55% of winning any point. Simulate several games and hence estimate the probability of the server winning the game. Investigate further.

Are you being Served? Arrival and Service Times

In the pedestrian crossing simulation we studied a queueing situation. You may have felt that the simple model used was not very realistic, and you probably suggested some improvements. For example, we assumed that pedestrians arrived at random at an average rate of one every 10 seconds. We modelled this by assuming that in a 5 second interval there was a 0.5 probability of one arrival and a 0.5 probability of no arrivals. Hence it was impossible to get more than one arrival in any 5 second period. This is actually quite a rough approximation: how could we improve it?

One obvious approach would be to consider shorter time intervals. We could keep the same average rate of arrivals by having time intervals of one second, and a probability of 0.1 for one arrival and 0.9 for no arrivals. It might be better to use still shorter time intervals such as 0.1 seconds or 0.01 seconds, with correspondingly modified probabilities: you might like to consider how short you think the intervals should be for an acceptable approximation.

If you try to re-run the pedestrian crossing simulation with time intervals of one second, you will find that to cover a 300 second time period you will need to generate five times as many random numbers as before. The simulation will therefore take about five times as long. We could possibly use a computer program to speed up the process but, like you, as the time intervals became smaller the computer would spend more actual time waiting for an arrival, so the simulation would take longer to run.

To improve both the accuracy and efficiency of a queueing simulation a different approach is needed. One possibility is to study the *inter-arrival times* or *arrival intervals*. These terms just mean the times between successive arrivals. For example, if the first pedestrian arrived at the crossing at time 2 seconds and the second pedestrian arrived at time 8 seconds then the inter-arrival time would simply be 6 seconds. We can then use random numbers to simulate directly the time between arrivals in a queue rather than look at each small time interval in turn. Try this out on the following problems.

Exercise 7B

1. Data is collected on the inter-arrival times of cars arriving at a petrol station. The arrival interval is measured to the nearest half minute and the data is given in the table opposite.

Inter-arrival times (minutes)	0.5	1	1.5	2	2.5
Percentage of occasions	10%	30%	30%	20%	10%

Use random number tables or a calculator to simulate the arrival times for the first 10 cars. A table like the one below might help, but leave room for about five more columns on the right.

Car	Random number	Arrival interval	Arrival time
1			
2			
3			
4			
5			
6			

2. Now suppose that the petrol station has just one petrol pump and that the following table gives the service times.

Service times (minutes)	1	1.5	2	2.5	3
Percentage of occasions	5%	25%	40%	20%	10%

Complete the simulation of the operation of the petrol station by adding extra columns to the table in question 1. Find the average time that customers spend waiting to be served.

3. Re-run the simulation in question 2 but with two petrol pumps. Do you think two pumps are justified in this situation?

The queueing discipline

We are now almost ready to begin simulations of various queueing situations. However a few other points are worth noting at this stage.

For any queueing system there is normally a set of rules, called the *queueing discipline*, which determines whose turn it is to be served next.

The most common queueing discipline is based on *First In, First Out* or FIFO for short. 'First come, first served' is a more common expression for the same thing.

To know exactly how a queueing system operates it is also necessary to make clear the number of servers and how the customers are assigned to the servers. For the petrol pump simulation in question 2 above we could say we have a single queue with one server, operating on FIFO. However we did not make it entirely clear how the situation in question 3 might work. It may be a single queue, multiple server system as shown in figure 7.1.

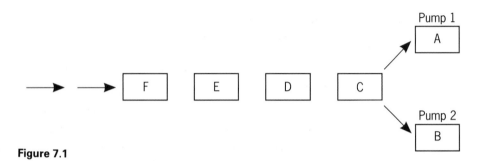

Figure 7.1

In this case the car at the head of the queue moves to the first free pump. Cars join the queue at one point at the end.

Alternatively in question 3 the two pumps might have separate queues, as in figure 7.2.

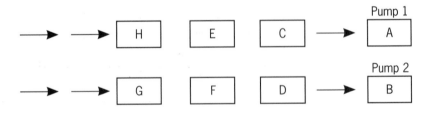

Figure 7.2

We now need to know how new arrivals decide which queue to join. Perhaps most of them would join the shortest of the two queues, or either queue at random if they were of the same length.

To get reliable information from any simulation it is necessary to run it several times. Since running one simulation is a fairly lengthy and repetitive process it is normal to use a computer for simulation problems. You can do this by programming the simulation for yourself or by using a special simulation package.

You may decide to use a computer for some of the questions in the following exercise, but most of them are simple enough to be tackled by

Decision and Discrete Mathematics

hand. Work in pairs or in a group if you wish, and attempt only a selection of the questions.

Exercise 7C

1. A petrol station has two car washes. The time taken for a car to be washed is always 12 minutes. During normal operating hours the following pattern of arrival intervals has been observed.

Interval between arrivals (minutes)	3	6	9	12	15
Frequency	30	45	15	5	5

(a) Find the average time between arrivals and hence state whether two car washes should be sufficient.

(b) Use random number tables or a calculator to simulate the arrival times of cars for a two hour period. Present your results in the form of a table like the one below, leaving room for about four more columns on the right for part (c), as shown.

Car	Random number	Arrival interval	Arrival time				
1							
2							
3							
4							

(c) The car washes are served by a single queue, the car at the head of the queue moving to the first available car wash. Complete the simulation of the operation of the car washes for the two hour period. You will need to add further columns to your table in part (b), probably with the headings 'Begins wash', 'Wash number (1 or 2)', 'Ends wash' and 'Waiting time'.

(d) Find the average waiting time and comment on your results.

2. A computer software company operates a telephone helpline for its customers. Calls to the helpline number are put into a queue. Recently there have been complaints of long delays before calls are answered during the busy period from 10.00 a.m. to 12.00 noon. At the moment there is just one employee who answers the helpline calls.

Exercise 7C continued

As part of study to improve customer service, data has been collected on the arrival intervals and time for each call. This is shown in the following tables.

Arrival interval (minutes)	1	2	3	4
Percentage of occasions	52	27	16	5

Call length (minutes)	1	2	3	4	5	6
Percentage of occasions	4	25	31	20	12	8

(a) Use the data to simulate the operation of the helpline for a period of about 30 minutes. Find the average waiting time.

(b) Do you think that more people should be employed on the helpline in the busy period? Perform an additional simulation to investigate the effect of one (or more) extra employees.

(c) Comment on your results.

3. A small building society branch has just one serving counter. During the lunchtime hours, long queues sometimes build up. The following data was collected in order to investigate the system.

Service time (minutes)	1	2	3	4	5
Percentage frequency	8	35	34	17	6

Arrival interval (minutes)	1	2	3
Percentage frequency	33	55	12

(a) Simulate the running of the branch for a period of about 60 minutes. Find the average waiting time for a customer.

(b) Find from the data above the average arrival interval and service time. Do you think a second counter is justified?

(c) Simulate the running of the branch with two counters.

(d) Comment on your results.

4. (a) Describe the operation for some real queueing situations with which you are familiar. You should state clearly the queueing discipline in operation.

(b) For a queueing system that has more than one server, discuss the relative advantages and disadvantages of 'single queue, multiple server' and 'multiple queue' systems.

5. At a fast food outlet the following pattern of arrival intervals has been observed.

Arrival interval (minutes)	0–1	1–2	2–3	3–4
Percentage frequency	30	40	20	10

(a) The fast food outlet opens at 6.00 p.m. each day. Use random numbers or a calculator to simulate the arrival times of the first 10 customers to the nearest 0.1 minutes.

(b) The service time can be modelled as a random time between 1 and 2 minutes. Complete the simulation of the queue for these customers.

(c) Do you think the outlet really will provide 'fast food'?

6. The cafeteria in a local park is self-service and there is one till. Customers go to the service counter, select various items, join a queue at the till and wait to receive service from the check-out operator. The following table gives a frequency distribution of observed inter-arrival times between 30 successive customers joining the queue at the till.

Inter-arrival time (seconds)	Number of arrivals
0–19	5
20–39	7
40–59	6
60–79	2
80–99	3
100–119	2
120–139	2
140–159	1
160–179	2
180–199	0

Decision and Discrete Mathematics

Exercise 7C continued

(a) Extend the table to include the relative frequencies and cumulative distribution of the inter-arrival times to three decimal places.

(b) Use the following four random numbers to find a sample of four inter-arrival times from this frequency distribution.

0.176   0.241   0.427   0.144

(c) The following is a sequence of randomly sampled service items (in seconds).

30   20   28   32   161

Use these, together with the inter-arrival times which you found in part (b), to carry out a simulation up to the time of the fourth arrival. Assume that the queueing discipline is FIFO and that the system starts as the first person arrives at time 0. For how long is the queue empty in this period?

(OXFORD)

7. A shop selling electrical equipment includes in its range of products a certain type of television set. The pattern of weekly demand observed for this particular television is given in the table.

Number of televisions demanded per week	0	1	2	3	4	5	6
Probability	0.15	0.25	0.25	0.15	0.10	0.05	0.05

The manager of the shop orders more televisions from the warehouse at the end of each week. These are delivered at the end of the next week, so that televisions ordered at the end of week 1 can be sold from the beginning of week 3. His current inventory policy is always to order $12 - n$ televisions, where n is the total number of televisions in stock at the end of the week.

(a) Simulate the operation of the inventory system for a period of 15 weeks. Set out your results in a table like the one shown.

Week	Stock at beginning	Random number	Demand	Order received	Stock at end of week
1	8			4	
2					
3					
4					
5					

(b) A simple model of the costs involved in this situation is as follows. Stockholding costs amount to £10 per week for every television in stock at the beginning of the week. Each television sold gives a net profit of £50 before stockholding costs are taken into account. Find the profit or loss made for the 15 weeks of your simulation.

(c) Suggest an alternative inventory policy, and perform another simulation to see whether your policy would produce greater profits. State clearly any assumptions made.

8. A friend of mine who manages a petrol station is keen to improve, if possible, her inventory policy. She has supplied me with the following information.
(i)   The station is open 6 days a week, closed Sundays.
(ii)   Demand for petrol is 1500–2500 gallons per day.
(iii) The tanks hold 30 000 gallons in total.
(iv) At the end of each day the amount of petrol in stock is checked. When the stock level falls below 20 000 gallons an order is placed for 15 000 gallons. The order lead-time is 4 working days, so an order placed at the end of day 1 is delivered at the end of the fifth working day.
(v)   Stockholding costs are 0.1% per day of the value of stock at the beginning of the day. The stock value is £2 per gallon. Fixed costs are £80 per day.
(vi) Net profit is 10p per gallon before stockholding and fixed costs are taken into account.

(a) Simulate the operation of the petrol station for a 20 day period. Find the profit or loss made.

(b) Suggest and investigate a different reorder policy. Petrol can be ordered in multiples of 1000 gallons, and the minimum order quantity is 10 000 gallons.

(c) State clearly any assumptions made in your simulations and comment on your results.

Investigations

1. Investigate a real queueing or stock control system. You will need to collect some data on the operation of the system and you should then set up a simulation. Suggest and investigate changes that may improve the system.

2. Write a computer program to simulate a simple queueing situation.

3. Use a spreadsheet package to simulate a simple stock control problem.

KEY POINTS

In this chapter we have looked at how some simple situations can be modelled using a simulation. After reading it you should

- know how to use a suitable random device such as a calculator to generate random numbers to perform a simulation;
- understand the following terms used in the context of queueing systems: *arrival interval, service time, queueing discipline*;
- remember that (as in all modelling situations) it is important to discuss carefully the assumptions made, and to compare the results of your simulation with real life.

8 Decision Analysis

An oil prospector is drilling for oil in a certain region. So far she has explored 10 sites and found oil in three of them. If oil is found at a site she makes a net profit of £2 million, but if no oil is found she makes a net loss of £1 million.

The prospector is given the chance to explore a new site. Based on the available evidence would you advise her to drill or not?

A geological survey team has just moved into the area, offering to carry out a survey of the new site for £250 000. If the result of the survey is promising then they estimate that there is a 60% chance of finding oil, but if the survey produces an unpromising outcome then there is only a 20% chance of finding oil at the site. The probability of a promising survey is estimated to be 50%.

Now what do you think the oil prospector should do: should she drill, commission a survey or forego the chance to explore the well?

Decisions have to be made in many situations like the one above where a chance element arises. In such situations there are often some stages at which we must make a decision, and some stages at which the outcome depends purely on chance. For example, the oil prospector has to decide whether to commission a survey or not (this is a decision stage), but the result of the survey is affected by chance. Once the survey result is known then she must decide whether or not to drill, but if she drills then chance determines whether oil is found.

In order to advise the oil prospector we need to develop some appropriate methods, and we shall do this by studying some simpler situations first.

Experiments

Two simple games of chance are described below. Play each game several times with a partner, one of you acting as banker (but don't use real money!).

When you have played each game try to answer the following questions:
(i) In whose favour is this game – the player's or the banker's?
(ii) How much does the player win or lose per game on average?

Game 1

You pay the banker £5 to spin two coins. For two heads you win £5 (and get your £5 stake back), for a head and a tail you win £2 (and get your stake back), for two tails your £5 stake is forfeit.

Game 2

You throw a die. If a 5 or a 6 shows the banker pays you £18; for any other number you lose £6. However, in the latter case you may if you wish throw the die again. This time if you throw a six you win £36 but otherwise you lose a further £6.

Analysis of the Games

Game 1

We can tabulate the profit to the player for each outcome as shown in the table.

Result	HH	HT or TH	TT
Probability	¼	½	¼
Profit (£)	+5	+2	−5

The player's average profit per game (or his expected profit) is therefore

$$\left(\frac{1}{4} \times £5\right) + \left(\frac{1}{2} \times £2\right) - \left(\frac{1}{4} \times £5\right) = £1$$

We conclude that the game is in the player's favour, and he can expect to gain £1 per game on average in the long run. The name given to the average gain in the long run is the *expected monetary value* (EMV for short). Hence in this game the player's EMV is £1 per game.

An alternative method of analysing this game is to use a tree diagram as in figure 8.1.

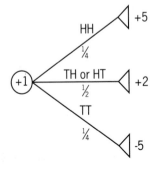

Figure 8.1

Notice that a triangle symbol is used to represent the outcomes and that we write the EMV of +1 in a circle or 'chance node'. We could even extend the diagram as shown in figure 8.2.

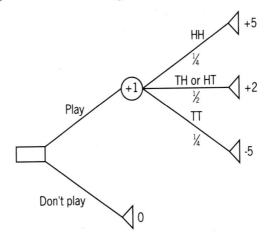

Figure 8.2

In this diagram we have also shown that the player can decide whether to play or not. There are now three types of node in the diagram:

* **triangles** to denote end pay-offs to the player;
* **rectangles** to denote stages at which the player makes a decision — *decision nodes*;
* **circles** to denote stages where chance determines the outcome — *chance nodes*.

This kind of diagram is called a *decision tree*. To use it to analyse the problem we work from the right hand side by labelling the pay-off boxes, then we calculate the EMV of +1 as we did above, and insert this in the chance node.

We now move back to the rectangular decision node and see that 'Play' has an EMV of +1, and 'Don't Play' an EMV of 0. On this basis we would decide to choose 'Play' and a double line is put through 'Don't Play' to show that this is an inferior option. This is shown in figure 8.3. We again, of course, conclude that the game is in the player's favour with an EMV of £1 per game.

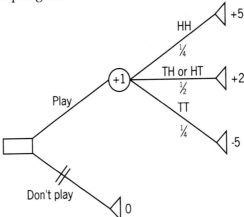

Figure 8.3

Game 2

Using the techniques described above you can now try to analyse this game. The decision tree is drawn for you in figure 8.4. Try to calculate the EMVs and to work out whether the player should agree to play this game before you read on!

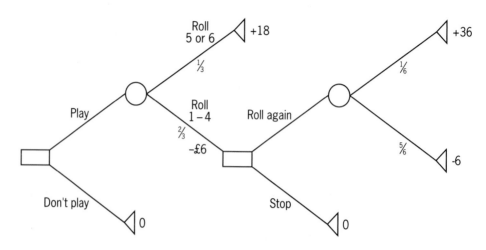

Figure 8.4

To work through this diagram, first find the EMV for the chance node on the right. This is

$$\left(\frac{1}{6} \times 36\right) - \left(\frac{5}{6} \times 6\right) = 1.$$

We now label this chance node with '+1'.

Moving back to the decision node in the middle of the diagram, we see that 'Roll again' has an EMV of +1 and 'Stop' has an EMV of 0. The double line is therefore placed across the 'Stop' option to denote that this is the inferior option. However, to find the EMV for this decision node, we have to allow for the £6 already lost in the first roll of the dice. Hence this node has an EMV of

$$-6 + 1 = -5$$

To complete the diagram the EMV for the chance node on the left of the diagram must be found. This is

$$(\tfrac{1}{3} \times 18) - (\tfrac{2}{3} \times 5) = \tfrac{8}{3}$$

$$= 2\tfrac{2}{3}$$

The final diagram is shown in figure 8.5.

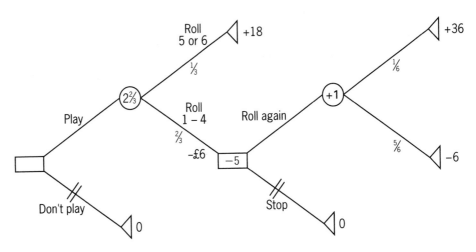

Figure 8.5

Having completed our analysis we would suggest the following strategy:

'Play the game, and if you roll a 1, 2, 3, or 4 on the first throw then roll again.'

With this strategy the player's EMV is £2⅔ per game.

The procedure developed above is usually referred to as the *EMV algorithm*. At each stage we take the decision which maximises our EMV. You may query whether decisions should always be made on the principle of maximising your EMV: this point is developed a little further in the following exercise.

Exercise 8A

Questions 1, 2 and 3 concern expectation or EMV only, questions 4 to 10 involve decision trees.

1. (a) In a simple game the player chooses a playing card from a normal pack of 52. For an ace he wins £20, for a king or queen £15, and for a Jack he pays the banker £50. If any other card is chosen he neither wins nor loses. What is his EMV per game?

   (b) A roulette wheel has 37 numbers into which the ball can drop. Eighteen of these are coloured red, eighteen are coloured black and the number 0 is not coloured. A player bets £1 on red. If the ball lands in a red number then he wins £1 and gets his £1 stake back, but for any other number his £1 stake is forfeit. Find his EMV per game.

2. (a) You play a game in which you will win £15 if you throw a total score of 11 or 12 with two dice; otherwise you will lose £2. What is your EMV per game?

   (b) What would your winnings need to be in part (a) instead of £15 to make your EMV zero?

Exercise 8A continued

3. (a) Three normal unbiased dice are thrown. Explain why

$$P \text{ (3 sixes)} = \tfrac{1}{216}$$

and find P (0 sixes), P (1 six) and P (2 sixes).

(b) In the game 'Crown and Anchor' a player pays £1 to throw three normal unbiased dice. If three sixes turn up he wins £3 and gets his £1 stake back, if two sixes turn up he wins £2 and gets his £1 stake back, if one six turns up he wins £1 and gets his £1 stake back. If no sixes turn up his £1 stake is forfeit. Find the player's EMV per game.

4. The organiser of a tennis tournament has to decide whether to take out pluvius insurance (that is insurance against rain on the day of the tournament). She estimates that on a fine day the tournament will make a profit of £5000 but on a wet day a loss of £10 000. The pluvius insurance will cost £1500 and pay out £6000 if it rains on the day of the tournament. The probability of rain is estimated to be $\tfrac{1}{5}$.

(a) Copy and complete the decision tree below to work out the organiser's best policy.

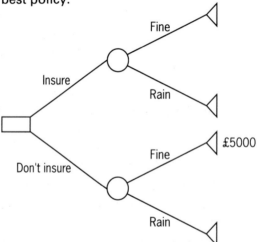

(b) The day before the tournament a weather forecaster now estimates the probability of rain to be $\tfrac{1}{3}$. If the organiser had used this probability would she have made the same decision?

5. In the game of 'Sprogget' the player rolls a normal die. If it lands on a one she wins £1, if it lands on a two she wins £2 and so on. However if she rolls a six she may roll the die again. On this second roll if a six is obtained then the player's £6 from the first round is forfeit; otherwise she wins a further £1 for a one, £2 for a two and so on as in the first round.

Construct a decision tree for this game. Find the player's optimal EMV per game and state the strategy that would obtain this EMV.

6. A company has just developed a new product and now a decision must be taken as to whether to launch the product without delay, to run a test market or to abandon the product. If the product is launched without delay then market research suggests that a strong market will occur with probability 0.3 and a weak market with probability 0.7. A strong market will bring a profit of £200 000, a weak market a profit of £50 000. To run a test market will cost £15 000 which will have to be deducted from profits, and this will give favourable or unfavourable indications. The probability of each of these outcomes is estimated to be 0.5. If the result of the test market is favourable then the probability of a strong market is now 80% but if the test market is unfavourable the probability of a weak market is 80%.

The product may be abandoned at any stage, either now or after the test market, and the technology developed may be sold to a rival company for a net profit of £90 000.

(a) Draw and label a decision tree to describe the above situation.

(b) Use the decision tree to say what decision should be taken and find the EMV associated with this plan.

(c) What is the maximum amount (instead of £15 000) that the company should be prepared to pay to run the test market?

7. Perform a decision tree analysis on the oil prospector's dilemma at the beginning of this chapter. Hence advise the oil prospector on her best course of action.

8. At a later date the oil prospector moves to a new region. Wells are now classified as 'soaking', 'wet' or 'dry'. Soaking wells bring a profit of £2.5 million, wet wells a profit of £0.5 million, dry wells a loss of £1 million. Of the twenty wells explored so far in this region, three have been soaking, six wet and the remaining ones dry.

(a) The prospector is given the chance to explore a new well. Based on current evidence should she accept or refuse the invitation to drill?

(b) A geologist offers to carry out a survey of the new site. The survey will indicate either 'promising' or 'unpromising' conditions, the probability of each of these outcomes being estimated at 0.5. The table below relates the results of the survey to the probable state of the well.

	Probability that well is soaking	Probability that well is wet	Probability that well is dry
Promising	0.2	0.4	0.4
Unpromising	0.1	0.2	0.7

Suppose the geologist offers to conduct the survey for £200,000. Draw a decision tree to represent the situation and hence find the oil prospector's best plan.

8

Exercise 8A continued

(c) What is the *maximum* amount that the oil prospector should be willing to pay for the survey?

9. You are fortunate enough to hold the winning ticket in a raffle in which the first prize is £100 000. As you go to claim your prize you are offered the following deal: you may either take your £100 000 prize or forego this for a second bet. In this second bet you have a 0.1 chance of winning £1 500 000 and a 0.9 chance of winning nothing.

(a) Draw a decision tree to represent the above situation and use the EMV algorithm to determine your optimal decision.

(b) Do you think you would really follow the decision in part (a)?

10. A game is played as follows. At each turn the player rolls two dice. If either die shows a six the player's score is zero and his turn is ended. If no sixes turn up then his score is taken to be the sum of the numbers showing, however in this case the player may elect to roll the dice again. On this second roll the same rules apply again. If a six shows his score for the turn is zero and his turn is ended, otherwise the score on the dice is added to the score from the first roll. In the latter case the player may then elect to roll the dice again with the same rules, and so on. Hence the player's turn continues until either he rolls a six (with either die), in which case his score is zero, or he elects to stop, in which case his score is the sum of numbers rolled so far.

Investigate the strategy the player should adopt to maximise his expected score at each turn.

KEY POINTS

After reading this chapter you should

- know how to calculate the average profit per game (i.e. the player's expected monetary value or EMV) in a simple game of chance;
- be able to construct a decision tree to analyse a more complicated situation, understanding that decision trees have three types of node: triangles for end pay-offs, circles for chance nodes and rectangular boxes for decision nodes;
- know that the EMV algorithm is based upon making decisions which maximise your EMV at each stage, and that when applied to a decision tree this means working from the right hand side towards the left.

9 Critical Path I

Every morning you toast three pieces of bread under a grill. The grill will take two pieces of bread at a time and takes 30 seconds to toast each side of the bread. The schedule for the operation could be as follows.

Toast one side of pieces A and B	30 s
Toast other side of pieces A and B	30 s
Toast one side of piece C	30 s
Toast other side of piece C	30 s
Total time	**120 s**

The schedule can be shortened, as shown in a famous wartime advertisement to encourage fuel saving, as follows.

Toast one side of pieces A and B	30 s
Toast one side of C and other side of A	30 s
Toast other side of B and C	30 s
Total time	**90 s**

This is a rather trivial example of how time can be saved by careful planning, but many similar opportunities arise in large scale construction and maintenance programmes. Critical Path Analysis is a technique that enables us to plan and monitor complex projects, so that they are approached and carried out as efficiently as possible.

First let us look at Critical Path Analysis in the context of a simple example.

Jane, Sue and Meena share a flat.

'Why didn't you wake me?' says Jane, emerging bleary eyed from her bedroom. 'I've got an interview at 9 o'clock and it's ten past eight already!'

'Don't worry', says Sue, 'I'll go and get your car from the garage and Meena will make you some breakfast. You go and shower and get dressed; you've got bags of time.'

Has Jane 'bags of time' with all this help or not?

9

Drawing the Network Diagram

First we need to list the activities and assess how long each will take.

Shower	3 minutes
Dress	8 minutes
Fetch car (from lock-up garage nearby)	7 minutes
Make breakfast	12 minutes
Eat breakfast	10 minutes
Drive to interview	20 minutes

Next we must determine the logical relationship between the activities. Some activities can take place concurrently, for example showering, making breakfast and fetching the car can all start immediately. Some activities cannot begin until others are completed, for example Jane cannot dress until she has showered and she cannot eat breakfast until both she has dressed and Meena has prepared her breakfast.

We could produce a list of all the activities and their immediately preceding activities.

	Activity	Immediately preceding activities
A	Shower	—
B	Dress	A
C	Fetch car	—
D	Make breakfast	—
E	Eat breakfast	B, D
F	Drive to interview	C, E

The start/finish of one or more activities is referred to as an *event*. In this example the first event marks the start of the activities 'make breakfast', 'shower' and 'fetch car'. Another event marks the completion of 'make breakfast' and 'dress' and the start of 'eat breakfast'.

We can now draw a network diagram to represent the sequence of activities.

Some rules for network diagrams

1. Activities are represented by arcs.

2. Events are represented by nodes (circles).

3. Events are numbered in such a way as to enable each activity to be referred to by a unique ordered pair of event numbers i, j with $j > i$. Dummy activities are introduced if necessary to ensure unique numbering. They are denoted by dotted lines and have zero duration (see Figure 92).

4. There should be one start and one finish node.

5. Details of the activity are written along the arc with the duration in brackets.

6. The length of arcs is not significant.

The network diagram for our example is shown in figure 9.1.

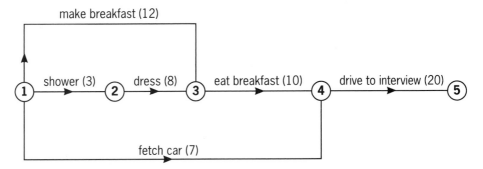

Figure 9.1

Identifying the Critical Path

It is clear that the duration of the whole operation is that of the longest path through the network. Any delay in the activities on this path will increase the duration of the whole operation. This path is called the *critical path* and the activities on it are referred to as *critical activities*.

To determine the critical path, we first move through the network from start to finish calculating the *earliest event times*. These are the earliest times that we can leave each of the events, bearing in mind that all activities leading into an event must be completed before we can leave it (figure 9.2).

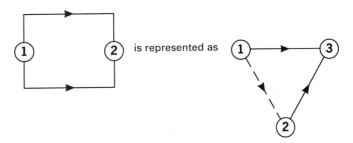

Figure 9.2

Earliest Event Times

The earliest event time for the start event is set to zero. In our example this will correspond to 8.10 am, and all times will be given in minutes after this start time. Beside each event we draw a double box, the left hand side will hold the earliest event time and the right hand side the *latest event time* which we shall meet later.

The earliest time 'dress' can begin is after 3 minutes, since Jane has to shower first and this takes 3 minutes. Although Jane can be showered and dressed in a total of 11 minutes, breakfast will not be ready until time 12, so the earliest time 'eat breakfast' can begin is 12. Whenever the start of an activity depends on two or more other activities being completed we must take the largest time so that all the relevant activities have been completed.

Continuing in this way we obtain the earliest event times shown in figure 9.3.

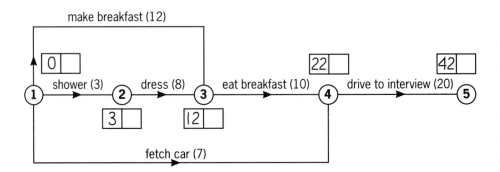

Figure 9.3

In general, to find an earliest event time, you have to consider each of the activities leading into an event. For each one, you add its duration to the earliest event time associated with its start. The earliest event time for the event under consideration is the largest of these values. The minimum completion time for the whole operation is the earliest event time for the final event.

Latest Event Times

The *latest event time* is the latest time we can leave an event if the operation is to be completed within its minimum completion time. Latest event times are established by working backwards through the network. First we make the latest event time for the finish event equal to its earliest event time.

Working backwards through our example, we see that the latest event time for event 4 is then 22, as Jane can't start driving to her interview any later without delaying the operation. Similarly, for event 3 the latest event time is 12.

The latest event time for event 2 will be 4, because we could leave dressing (which takes 8 minutes) until time 4 without delaying the start of eating breakfast. There are three activities starting from event 1. We must choose the latest event time that will not lead to any delay, so we must choose the minimum of $(12 - 12)$, $(4 - 3)$ and $(22 - 7)$, which is 0.

Decision and Discrete Mathematics

Otherwise breakfast will not be ready on time. The resulting diagram is shown in Figure 9.4.

If we put the same numbers in the two halves of the finish event box, we should always work back to (0,0) in the start event box. This is a useful check on your working.

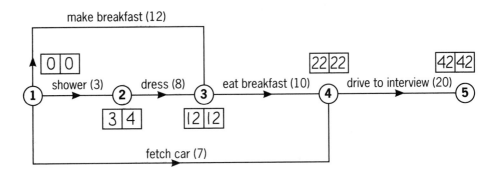

Figure 9.4

In general, to find a latest event time, you have to consider each of the activities that begin at an event. For each one, you subtract its duration from the latest event time associated with the end of the activity. The latest event time for the event under consideration is the smallest of these.

Critical activities are ones that must start and finish on time if the operation is not to be delayed. The set of critical activities is the critical path. Looking at our network diagram it should be clear that preparing breakfast, eating breakfast and driving to the interview are critical. Any delay in these activities will extend the time for the operation beyond its minimum of 42 minutes.

Jane should get to her interview on time, and will in fact have 8 minutes to spare if all activities on the critical path are completed on time. Perhaps Sue need not fetch the car after all!

In general, if the difference between the earliest event time at the beginning of an activity and the latest event time at the end of the activity equals the duration of that activity, then the activity is critical. This fact would be useful if we were wanting to write a computer program to find critical activities.

The non-critical activities have some spare time (called *float*) associated with them. For example, fetching the car takes only 7 minutes, and the car is not required until time 22, so there can be a delay of 15 minutes without affecting the overall duration of the operation. In general, if the difference between the earliest time at which an activity can begin and the latest time at which it can be completed is greater than its duration, the activity will have float. We will consider float in more detail later in

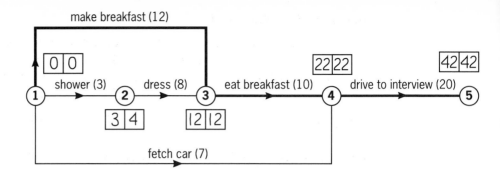

Figure 9.5

the chapter. The completed network with critical activities highlighted is shown in figure 9.5.

Float

We can see that there is one minute to spare for the two activities 'shower' and 'dress'. It is one minute shared between them. If Jane takes an extra minute in the shower then there is no spare time to get dressed. Similarly if she wants to give herself that extra minute to dress, she must keep her shower to three minutes. Alternatively she can spend an extra half minute on each activity and so on. This kind of float is referred to as *interfering* float.

The spare time associated with fetching the car (15 minutes) belongs just to that activity and is referred to as *independent* float. Use could be made of this float to allow Sue to make breakfast before fetching the car. So even if Meena were not available the operation could still be completed in 42 minutes. In fact there would still be 3 minutes of spare time associated with fetching the car, as shown in the amended network in figure 9.6.

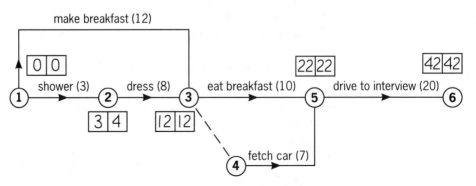

Figure 9.6

In general for activity (i, j):

> interfering float = latest event time for event j − earliest event time for event i − duration of activity.
>
> independent float = earliest event time for event j − latest event time for event i − duration of activity.

Can you see why these formulae give the required results?

Computer Programs for Critical Path Analysis

Many computer programs are available to carry out critical path analysis. It is when using certain packages that the activity numbering convention becomes particularly important. A typical output from such a package applied to our example is given below.

		Activities		Earliest activity times		Latest activity times		Float	
i	j		Dur.	St.	End	St.	End	Inter.	Indep.
1	2	Shower	3	0	3	1	4	1	0
1	3	*Make breakfast*	12	0	12	0	12	0	0
1	4	Fetch car	7	0	7	15	22	15	15
2	3	Dress	8	3	11	4	12	1	0
3	4	*Eat breakfast*	10	12	22	12	22	0	0
4	5	*Drive to interview*	20	22	42	22	42	0	0

(Critical activities in italics.)

Other programs simply require a list of activities and durations together with the preceding activities. For example, the program in the Spode Group's 'Decision Maths Software' accepts input in the following form.

Activity		Duration	Preceding activities
A	Shower	3	—
B	Dress	8	A
C	Fetch car	7	—
D	Make breakfast	12	—
E	Eat breakfast	10	B, D
F	Drive to interview	20	C, E

The output from the program is shown below.

Three Girls

CAN	Activity Description	Preceding Activities	Succeeding Activities	Activity Duration	EST	EFT	LST	LFT
1	Shower	—	2	3	0	3	1	4
2	Dress	1	5	8	3	11	4	12
3	Fetch Car	—	6	7	0	7	15	22
4	Make breakfast	—	5	12	0	12	0	12
5	Eat breakfast	2 4	6	10	12	22	12	22
6	Drive to interview	3 5	—	20	22	42	22	42

Exercise 9A

1. A precedence network for the cleaning of an industrial boiler is given below. The activity times are in hours. The boiler is to be brought back into service as quickly as possible. How quickly can the operation be completed and which are the critical activities?

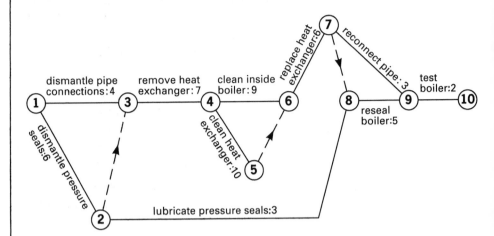

2. A construction project has been represented in network form below.

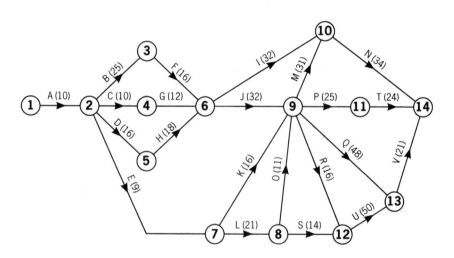

Analyse the network to determine how much time will be required to complete the project, and to identify which activities lie on the critical path.

An important use of critical path analysis is in the continuous monitoring of a project whilst it is under way. Use it to tackle the following problems.

(a) What would be the effect on the operation as a whole if a reduction in the resources available for activity H caused its duration to be increased to 28 days?

Exercise 9A continued

(b) The supervisor in charge of activity I wants her team to work overtime to reduce the duration of this activity to 24 days. If you were the person in overall control of the project, how would you respond to this request?

(c) Money is available to spend on extra machinery for either activity B or activity Q. The extra machine for activity B will reduce its duration to 20 days, a saving of 5 days. For the same outlay a machine could be purchased to cut the time of activity Q by 50%. What would you advise?

(d) At the end of 50 days you are advised that activities A, B, C, D, E, F, G and H are completed, but that due to late delivery of materials activity K cannot be started for another 14 days. The company will have to pay a penalty if the project takes more than 175 days. Assess the effect of this delay and advise accordingly.

3. Draw a network and carry out the analysis for the following activities involved in building a house. What is the minimum completion time and which activities are critical?

Activity		Duration (days)	Preceding activities
A	Prepare foundations	7	—
B	Order bricks	5	—
C	Order tiles	12	—
D	Lay drains	7	A
E	Erect shell	10	A, B
F	Roofing	4	C, E
G	Flooring	5	F
H	Plumbing	12	D, G
I	Glazing	1	G
J	Wiring	10	G
K	Plastering	6	H, J
L	Fittings	2	I, K
M	Clear site	2	I, K
N	Paint and clean	6	L
O	Lay paths	2	M

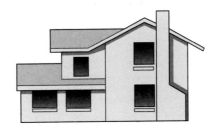

Exercise 9A continued

4. The stages involved in recording and promoting a compact disc are shown in the table below.

Activity		Duration (weeks)	Preceding activities
A	Tape the performance	10	–
B	Design the cover	9	–
C	Book adverts in press	3	–
D	Tape to CD	2	A
E	Produce cover	4	B
F	Packing	1	D, E
G	Promotion copies to radio etc.	1	D, E
H	Dispatch to shops	3	F
I	Played on radio	2	G
J	Adverts in press etc.	1	C, H, I

Draw a network and carry out the analysis to find how long the project will take and which activities are critical.

5. For an airline, an aircraft on the ground is an aircraft not earning money. However, safety is of paramount importance and this requires regular thorough maintenance. Critical path analysis has been widely used in planning such maintenance schedules.

Here is a much simpler maintenance situation for you to analyse. You take your car into the garage and fill up with petrol and have a few routine checks and jobs done. You can assume that the garage is well staffed and that you can just sit back and let their team swing into action. How long is it all going to take?

Activity	Duration (seconds)
Fill petrol tank	240
Wash windscreen	60
Check tyre pressure and inflate	180
Open bonnet	10
Check oil and top up	120
Check and fill radiator	60
Check and fill battery	60
Close bonnet	10
Pay bill	90

6. Four people are travelling by car when they have a flat tyre. Here is a list of the activities involved in changing the wheel. How long will they be delayed if they work together efficiently to change it?

	Activity	Duration (minutes)
A	Locate which tyre has the puncture	1
B	Unlock boot	0.5
C	Get tool-kit from the boot	1
D	Get jack from the boot	2
E	Get spare wheel from boot	2
F	Fix jack under car	2
G	Remove hub-cap	0.5
H	Loosen wheel nuts	2
I	Jack up car clear of ground	3
J	Remove wheel nuts	2
K	Remove wheel from hub	0.5
L	Put spare wheel on hub	1
M	Loosely replace wheel nuts	2
N	Put punctured wheel in boot	2
O	Lower jack	2
P	Remove jack from under car	1
Q	Tighten wheel nuts	2
R	Replace jack in boot	2
S	Replace tool-kit in boot	1
T	Replace hub-cap	0.5
U	Lock boot	0.5

KEY POINTS

The stages in a critical path analysis are as follows.

1. Prepare the network
- Make a list of the activities involved in the operation with their durations.
- Decide on the logical sequence of activities: which activities can go on at the same time, which cannot begin until others are completed.

2. Draw the network
- Activities are represented by arcs.
- Events, i.e. the starts and finishes of activities, are represented by nodes.
- There should be one start and one finish node for the whole project.
- Use dummy activities to ensure unique numbering of activities.

3. Analyse the network
- Calculate the earliest event times by working through the network from start to finish.
- Calculate the latest event times by working backwards through the network.
- Identify the critical path.
- Calculate the float on non-critical activities.

10 Critical Path II

When Mr and Mrs Jaffrey go out together in the car they get away more quickly than when Mr Jaffrey goes out on his own. Here are the activities involved in each case.

MR JAFFREY

Walk to garage doors	10 seconds
Open garage door	5
Walk to car	5
Enter and start car	10
Drive car out of garage	5
Walk back to garage	5
Shut garage door	5
Walk back to car	5
Drive off	5
TOTAL	**55 SECONDS**

MR AND MRS JAFFREY

MR JAFFREY		*MRS JAFFREY*	
Walk to garage doors	10	Walk to car by back door	10
Open garage door	5	Enter and start car	10
Wait for Mrs Jaffrey to drive out of garage	10	Drive car out of garage	5
Shut garage door	5	Wait for Mr Jaffrey to close garage door and get in the car	10
Get in car	5		
		Drive off	5
		TOTAL	**40 SECONDS**

In our critical path analysis to date we have assumed that there were enough people available to carry out concurrent activities. As we see in the example above, Mr and Mrs Jaffrey together can get away in 40 seconds compared with the 55 seconds that it takes Mr Jaffrey on his own. Mr Jaffrey is kept fully occupied when he is alone, but he and his wife have some waiting time when they are both involved. Efficient planning must take account of the resources (people and equipment) required at different stages of the operation and try to make use of them in the most efficient way. We saw in the 'Three Girls' example of the previous chapter that Jane really only needed one helper.

The drawing of a *cascade chart*, which shows the information in the completed network diagram in the form of bars drawn against a time scale, gives a different perspective on the operation and is a necessary first step in considering resource allocation. Two possible cascade charts for the 'Three Girls' example are shown in figure 10.1. Activities are represented by bars of length proportional to their duration and critical activities are shown shaded. It has been assumed that activities start at their earliest possible times. The relationship between activities is shown by dotted vertical lines. If an activity is delayed it cannot move past one of these dotted lines: the effect will actually be to push the line to the right, along with those activities beyond it.

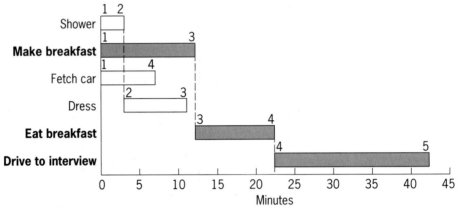

Figure 10.1(a)

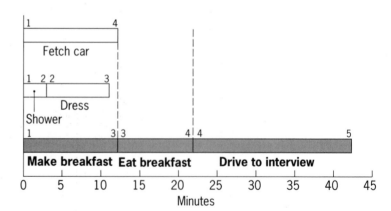

Figure 10.1(b)

In the first chart, the order of activities is that given in the computer output table in the previous chapter, i.e. activity order (i, j) sorting first on i and then on j to give (1,2), (1,3), (1,4), (2,3), (3,4), (4,5). In the second chart, the critical activities have been put together and the others grouped appropriately.

If 'Shower' is delayed it will push 'Dress' on. This is obvious in b) and is shown by the vertical dotted line in a). A delay in 'Dress' longer than one minute will push 'Eat breakfast' on. The effect of a delay in 'Fetch car' is probably more clearly seen in b): when the bar reaches the dotted line it will affect 'Drive to interview'. In a) the dotted vertical line

Decision and Discrete Mathematics

between the 3s appears to bar the path of this activity but in fact this link 'flies over' activity (1,4).

We can see from this that the order in which the activities are placed on the cascade chart greatly affects the ease of interpretation. For this reason, *cascade activity numbers* (CANs) are sometimes allocated to define a suitable ordering for the chart. It is easy to produce a logical order for a small number of activities by hand, but some operations have hundreds of activities and require a computer to carry out the analysis. It is these cases, as we have seen many times before, that demand an efficient algorithm such as the one shown in figure 10.2.

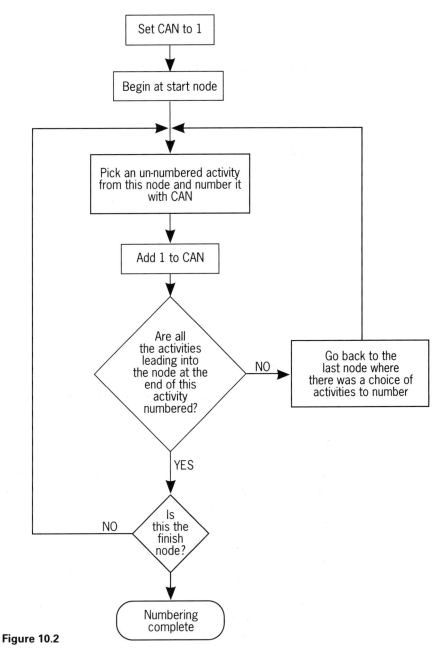

Figure 10.2

For the 'Three Girls' example this would lead to the cascade chart shown below.

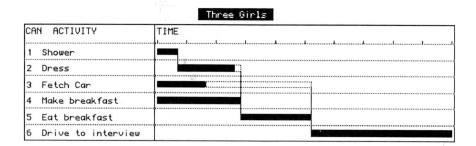

(Output from C.P.A. program by Centre for Innovation in Mathematics Teaching, Exeter)

From the cascade chart it is a simple matter to draw a resource histogram to show the number of people required at any given time. Figure 10.3(a) shows the resources needed for the operation as originally defined, with all activities starting as soon as possible. In figure 10.3(b), float available on the activity 'Fetch car' has been used to smooth out the fluctuation in the resources histogram, a process referred to as *resource levelling*.

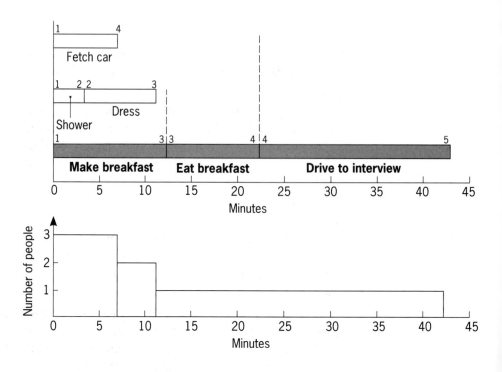

Figure 10.3 (a)

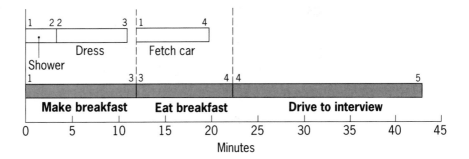

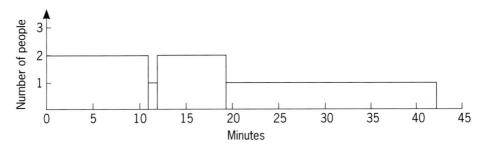

Figure 10.3(b)

The way in which resource levelling is carried out depends on what the overriding objective is. There are three possibilities.

- **Minimise total time**
  This is typically the case with maintenance, when we want a piece of equipment to be out of operation for as short a time as possible. For example the overhaul of the industrial boiler in the last chapter or the routine maintenance of aircraft between flights would need to be planned in this way.

- **Minimise total cost**
  When time is not at a premium, for example when demand for a facility or piece of equipment is seasonal, it is possible to plan in this way. For example, alterations to a seaside resort hotel might be allowed to go on for a long period over the winter, so as to minimise costs.

- **Make maximum use of resources (people and equipment)**
  If we need to work with a fixed team of workers, or if we want to avoid hiring two cement mixers when, with careful planning, one will do, then this kind of planning is appropriate.

The actual objective will often be some combination of all three.

Exercise 10A

1. Analyse the production of a meal of toad-in-the-hole, potatoes and cabbage, followed by apple pie and custard, the activities in which are listed below.

   (a) What is the shortest time in which it could be prepared, and how many people would be required?

   (b) If time were not critical, consider how the best use could be made of limited resources.

Activity	Duration (minutes)
Grill sausage	8
Make batter	6
Make apple pie	15
Prepare potatoes	6
Prepare cabbage	4
Cook sausage and batter together	35
Cook potatoes	25
Cook cabbage	8
Cook apple pie	30
Lay table	5
Make custard	8

2. Construct a network either by hand or using a computer package, to analyse an annual maintenance which consists of the activities listed below.

Activity	Immediately preceding activity	Duration (days)	Resources (Number of workers)
A	—	1	1
B	A	2	1
C	B	4	1
D	A	3	1
E	C	14	1
F	C	14	2
G	C	16	2
H	D, G	12	2
I	D, G	14	3
J	D, G	10	1
K	H	5	1
L	I	4	2
M	J	6	1
N	E, F, K, L, M	3	2

   (a) Calculate the minimum time required to complete the project and determine which activities are critical.

(b) Calculate the amount of spare time available on the other activities, distinguishing between interfering and independent float. List those activities which are 'sub-critical', in this case defined as the ones with a float of less than 7 days.

(c) Draw a cascade chart for the operation, assuming that activities begin as soon as possible. Determine how many workers are required on each day of the project and show this manpower schedule graphically.

(d) Describe in detail the effect on the operation if only 5 workers are available. You may assume that each worker can carry out any of the activities.

3. Draw and analyse the network for the project whose activities are listed below.

Activity	Immediately preceding activity	Duration (days)
A	—	8
B	—	4
C	A	2
D	A	10
E	B	5
F	C, E	3

For this project the duration of any of the activities can be accelerated, at a cost. The table below shows the normal duration and cost for each activity, the minimum time to which its duration can be reduced and the cost for this time. If an activity is accelerated to a duration greater than the minimum, the cost is calculated on a pro-rata basis, for example the accelerated cost of activity A to 7 days would be £150.

Activity	Duration	Normal cost (£)	Duration	Accelerated cost (£)
A	8	100	6	200
B	4	150	2	350
C	2	50	1	90
D	10	100	5	400
E	5	100	1	200
F	3	80	1	100

Assuming that the only possible way of reducing the total time is by increasing the costs, which activity or activities would you recommend should be accelerated if
(i) 2 days
(ii) 7 days
reduction in total time were necessary?

4. Write an algorithm to produce the (i, j) numbering of activities, given a list of the activities and those that immediately precede each one.

Investigations

1. Draw cascade charts and investigate the resources for questions 5 and 6 on pp 124–5.

2. Carry out a Critical Path Analysis for a project of your choice. Here are some suggestions.
   (a) Putting on a school play.
   (b) Giving a dinner party.
   (c) Starting a mini-enterprise.

Practical Activity

1. In drawing cascade charts we have so far positioned the non-critical activities so that they start at the earliest possible time. If the start of an activity were delayed for a time within the available float, we would need to redraw the bar for that activity to show the new situation. If the delay were greater than the available float there would be a knock-on effect on other activities and we would need to redraw the whole chart.

   To overcome this problem construct a 'dynamic' cascade chart using strips of card sliding in channels to represent the activities. The channels could be fixed on to a piece of pegboard and pegs used to mark the beginning and end of the channels in which the activities can slide. Try to devise suitable linkages to show inter-relationships between activities.

   An example is shown in the drawing below.

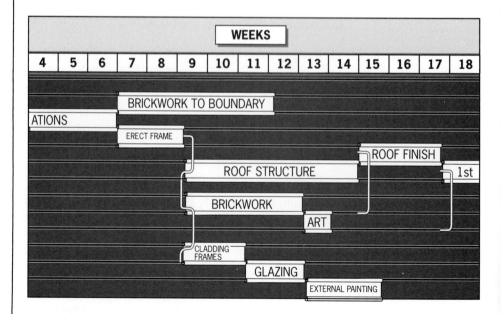

KEY POINTS

When you have read this chapter you should

- be able to construct a cascade chart;
- understand the importance of ordering of activities;
- understand how you can utilise float;
- be able to construct a resource histogram from a cascade chart;
- be able to suggest how to utilise float to produce a more even use of human resources.

Answers to selected exercises

3 FINDING THE SHORTEST PATH

Exercise 3A

1. (i)   F P O M N J A; 24
   (ii)   B I H G; 25
   (iii) E D C Q A; 23
   (iv) H I A Q; 22
   (v)   N K L Q D C; 22
2. (a) C Q L M O G; 21
   (b) G P F E D C; 26
3. F P O M N K L; 23
   G O M N K L; 21
   H I A J K L; 25
4. Before NK closed: G O M N K L; 21
   After NK closed: G O M N J K L; 27.
   The journey is therefore 6 mins. longer.
5. O M N H I; 21
6. J K L M N; 15
   J A Q L M N; 25 is the shortest route if KL not used, so if delay > 10 mins. it
   would be quicker to go round.
7. C has the better average time to all other nodes but depends on your criteria.

Exercise 3B

1. (a) S P Q R T or S U V W T; 15
   (b) S A B F E D T; 8
   (c) S B F J T; 12
2. (a) L.A. → San Fran. → Salt Lake → Omaha → Chicago; 42
   (b) New Orleans → Chicago → Omaha → Denver; 34
   (a) L.A. → Santa Fe → Denver → Omaha → Chicago; 42 (no better).
   (b) New Orleans → El Paso → Santa Fe → Denver → ; 31 (better).
3. C: 3 + 4 + 2 + 2 + 3 = 14
4. (a) (i)   On to M5 at junction 6 and off at 10, distance 40
       (ii)   Same as (i)
       (iii) 87 mph (illegal) if you joined M5 at junction 4
       (iv) Yes: join M5 at junction 7
   (b) (i)   On to M5 at junction 9, off at 6
       (ii)   Don't use motorway
       Still use M5 but on at junction 9 and off at 7.

4 MINIMUM CONNECTOR PROBLEM

The solution to the initial cable TV problem is 289 miles.

Exercise 4A

1. 286
2. 187
3. 463
4. 523

Exercise 4B

1. 82
2. 66

5 THE TRAVELLING SALESMAN PROBLEM

The pop tour is at present 1587 miles but can be improved to 1356 with the route London → Brighton → Bristol → Birmingham → Manchester → Liverpool → Glasgow → Aberdeen → Newcastle → Sheffield → Nottingham → Oxford → London. (This solution was obtained with the MEI Travelling Salesman Package.)

Exercise 5A
The optimal tour is:
Worcester → Evesham → Tewkesbury → Cheltenham → Gloucester → Ross → Hereford → Malvern → Worcester; 104 miles

Exercise 5B
1. Upper bound 58, lower bound 40
2. Upper bound 164, lower bound 101
3. Rough upper bound 1332
   Lower bounds:

Town deleted	
London	793
Chester	975
Dover	793
Glasgow	**1022**
Oxford	878
Plymouth	880

   The optimal tour is:
   London → Plymouth → Glasgow → Chester → Oxford → Dover → London; 1256

Exercise 5C
1. Weston → Burnham → Bridgwater → Glastonbury → Wells → Bath → Cheddar → Weston; 95
2. Birmingham → Gloucester → Hereford → Shrewsbury → Stoke → Sheffield → Nottingham → Northampton → Birmingham; 357
3. St. Hélier → Corbière → Devil's Hole → Trinity Church → Rozel → Mount Orgueil → St. Hélier → Le Rocq → St. Hélier; 37.5
4. Optimum distance 378
6. (b) Minimum spanning tree distance 25
   (c) Upper bound 25
7. (a) Strawberry → orange → lemon → lime → raspberry → strawberry; 73 mins.
   (b) No; this gives 77 mins.

Investigation
Two tours: A → B → C → A and A → D → E → A; total length 237

6 THE ROUTE INSPECTION PROBLEM

Exercise 6A
1. (a) Sum of arc lengths + 15
   (b) Sum of arc lengths + 34
2. (a) Sum of arc lengths + 2900
   (b) Sum of arc lengths + 2800
3. Sum of arc lengths + 33
4. Sum of arc lengths + 18
5. Sum of arc lengths + 23

7 SIMULATION

Exercise 7C

1. (a) 6.3 mins
3. Average arrival interval = 1.79 mins
   Average service time = 2.78 mins

8 DECISION ANALYSIS

Exercise 8A

1. (a) 0
   (b) $- \frac{1}{37}$ p
2. (a) $- £\frac{21}{36}$
   (b) £22
3. (a) $\frac{125}{216}$, $\frac{75}{216}$, $\frac{15}{216}$
   (b) $- £\frac{2}{27}$
4. (a) Do not insure
   (b) No
5. EMV = 3.75. Roll again if possible
6. (b) Run test market and launch if favourable; otherwise abandon.
   EMV = £115 000
   (c) £35 000
7. Survey and drill only if promising.
   EMV = £0.15 million
8. (a) Refuse (EMV $= -$ £0.025 million)
   (b) Abandon project (survey too expensive to give positive EMV)
   (c) £150 000
9. (a) Take the bet.

9 CRITICAL PATH I

Exercise 9A

1. 36 hours. Critical activities: Dismantle pressure seals, Remove heat exchanger, Clean heat exchanger, Replace heat exchanger, Reseal boiler, Test boiler.
2. Time required 170 days. Critical path A, B, F, J, R, U, V.
   (a) Time required increased to 173 days.
   New critical path: A, D, H, J, R, U, V.
   (b) I not critical, so no benefit.
   (c) B, since it is on critical path. New time required 165 days, same critical path.
   (d) Time required 176 days. Critical path from this point is K, R, U, V.
   In order to avoid penalty speed up one of these activities by 1 day.
3. Shortest time 52 days. Critical activities A, E, F, G, H, K, L, N.
4. Shortest time 18 weeks. Critical activities B, E, F, H, J.

10 CRITICAL PATH II

Exercise 10A

2. 44 days. Critical activities A, B, C, G, I, L, N

Float			
	D	19	independent
	E	20	independent
	F	20	independent
	H/K	1	shared
	J/M	2	shared

Sub-critical activities H, J, K, M.

If only 5 workers are available the project will need 54 days.

3. Original cost £580
    (a) Reduce duration of A to 2 days at a total cost of £680
    (b) Reduce A to 6 days, D to 5 days and F to 2 days at a total cost of £990.

Index

Decision and Discrete Mathematics